D1486602

RUNNER'S WORLD COMPLETE GUIDE TO RUNNING

THIS IS THE SCIENCE OF SOFT.
LET'S MAKE EXCELLENT HAPPEN.
FRESH FOAM 980
Impossibly soft, yet stable. It does exist and it's unlike anything you've ever felt before.
THIS IS #FRESHFOAM. THIS IS #RUNNOVATION.
new balance.com/running
©2014 New Balance Athletic Shoe, Inc.

RUNNER'S WORLD

EDITOR-IN-CHIEF DAVID WILLEY

EDITOR JOHN ATWOOD
EXECUTIVE EDITOR TISH HAMILTON
EDITORS AT LARGE AMBY BURFOOT, MARK REMY
MANAGING EDITOR SUZANNE PERREAULT
ARTICLES EDITOR KATRIN McDONALD NEITZ
SENIOR EDITORS JEFF DENGATE,
CHRISTINE FENNESSY, JOANNA SAYAGO GOLUB
ASSOCIATE EDITOR NICK WELDON
ASSISTANT MANAGING EDITOR LINDSAY BENDER
CONTRIBUTING COPY EDITORS CHRIS M. JUNIOR, BARBARA WEBB
EXECUTIVE ASSISTANT KIRA WRIGHT

ART + PHOTOGRAPHY
DESIGN DIRECTOR BENJAMEN PURVIS
PHOTO DIRECTOR MICHELE ERVIN
ASSOCIATE PHOTO EDITOR RENEE KEITH
ASSISTANT ART DIRECTOR TARA MAIDA
CONTRIBUTING DESIGNER TARA LONG
PRODUCTION COORDINATOR JAMES CAVALIERI

SENIOR VICE PRESIDENT, PUBLISHING DIRECTOR
CHRISTOPHER L. LAMBIASE

ASSOCIATE PUBLISHER/MARKETING
SUSAN HARTMAN
ASSOCIATE PUBLISHER/ADVERTISING
MOLLY O'KEEFE CORCORAN

ADVERTISING
ADVERTISING DIRECTOR PAUL COLLINS
PAUL.COLLINS@RODALE.COM

NEW YORK
733 THIRD AVENUE, 10TH FLOOR, NEW YORK, NY 10017-3204
PHONE: 212-808-1474
NEW ENGLAND ADVERTISING MANAGER AMY VORLAND TOTA
AMY.TOTA@RODALE.COM

LOS ANGELES
880 APOLLO STREET, SUITE 329, EL SEGUNDO, CA 90245-4709
PHONE: 310-252-7518
INTERACTIVE SALES MANAGER TARA SALCIDO
TARA.SALCIDO@RODALE.COM

SAN FRANCISCO
NORTHWEST SALES REPRESENTATIVE NICHOLAS FREEDMAN
NICK@MEDIAHOUNDSINC.COM PHONE: 707-775-3376

DIRECTOR, NEWSSTAND SALES MARK BUCKALEW
DIRECTOR, DIRECT STORE DELIVERY PHILIP TRINKLE

PRODUCTION
PRODUCTION SPECIALIST SUE ROECKER
PRINT PRODUCTION MANAGER KELLY McDONALD

RODALE.

J.I. Rodale
Founder, 1942-1971

Robert Rodale
Chairman of the Board and CEO, 1971-1990

Ardath Rodale
CEO and Chief Inspiration Officer, 1990-2009

Maria Rodale
Chairman and Chief Executive Officer

Rodale Inc., 400 South 10th Street, Emmaus, PA 18098-0099
610-967-5171
rodale.com

Portions of this publication appeared previously in Runner's World Magazine.
Permission granted by Rodale Inc., Emmaus, PA 18098-0099.

IMAGE: THOMAS MACDONALD

FROM THE EDITOR

> **DO YOU REALLY** need a complete guide to running? After all, just about anyone can put one foot in front of the other and gradually start moving faster—that's one of the inherent joys of our sport. But, like most of the fun things in life, with a little guidance you (and I) can do it even better.

That's where this 176-page tome comes in—a *Runner's World* "best of" special, containing hundreds of top tips from experts and the editors of the world's leading running magazine. We've packed it with easy-to-follow training schedules, proven weight-loss plans, workouts to help you run faster, and much more.

Whether you're just getting started or you're a seasoned athlete chasing a PR, this book can help you run better—which, according to "49 Reasons to Love Running" (page 26), can lead to more enjoyment in other parts of your life, too!

DAVID WILLEY
EDITOR-IN-CHIEF

CONTENTS

p.18 **p.34** **p.68** **p.108**

A FRESH START

Our guide to becoming a runner—whether you're new to the sport or you just want to know more

ANYBODY CAN BE A RUNNER. The sport's inclusiveness is part of its appeal. But how do you actually become a runner? Tie your shoes and go? In essence, running is that simple. That's also part of its appeal. But as you get going, questions arise: Should I run for 20 minutes or 30?

Is walking okay? If I've run before, do I need to start right back at the beginning? Over the following pages, you'll find the answers, along with everything else you need to get started on a running program.

1) BEFORE TAKING YOUR FIRST STEP
MAKE SURE YOU'RE WELL PREPARED FOR YOUR FIRST RUN

Many new runners are reluctant to spend money or time on the sport before they get started because they don't know if they'll stick with it. But getting started will be easier if you commit some time and do a bit of planning first. It may be overwhelming to begin with—thoughts of new shoes, training plans, and races can get to be too much, so we've made it really simple for you to get started.

GET A CHECKUP

You may feel fine, but if you're a man over 45 or a woman over 55, and especially if you have risk factors for heart disease (obesity, family history, hypertension, high cholesterol), get your doctor's clearance to start exercising. If you have cardiovascular disease, which you may not know about, you could be at greater risk of suffering a heart attack. A plan to start running is a good excuse to get a checkup scheduled.

SET A GOAL

"Your goals become incentives," says coach Nick Anderson. "If you don't set a target, you'll get bored. A target might be to run for 30 minutes continuously, or it might be a 5-K race that you want to do without having to walk." Choose a realistic goal while you build your base levels of fitness.

TAKE IT EASY

Beginners can be enthusiastic, but don't push too hard. "I always start new runners gently," says coach Richard Holt. "It's vital not to let eagerness lead to early injuries through overtraining, but to build a platform from which to progress later."

BUY RUNNING SHOES

"Often beginners are reluctant to buy a pair of running shoes in case they decide not to keep it up," says Ben Noad, runner and marketing manager for specialist shop Runner's Need. "Shoes are the most important piece of gear—you can start in any clothes, but you must wear decent shoes. They'll pay for themselves in keeping you injury-free." Cross-trainers, tennis shoes, and other athletic footwear don't have enough cushioning to handle running's impact—nor does the pair of shoes you wore two years ago, so buy new ones. We'll tell you how later in the chapter.

IMAGE: TIMOTHY ARCHIBALD ILLUSTRATIONS: SUPERCORN

GETTING STARTED

2) HOW TO START
TAKING YOU THROUGH YOUR FIRST THREE WEEKS OF RUNNING

First-run horror stories are common, but avoidable. "Starting or returning to a sport is going to be a little uncomfortable because you're not conditioned to it," says coach Greg McMillan. Having been a runner before or being fit doesn't exempt you from this reality. Elizabeth Hufton, who recently returned to running after more than a year off, says, "At first my legs gave out with a few minutes' running. I'd cross-trained, but it was a shock to find how much running fitness I'd lost."

Minimize discomfort by taking walk breaks and keeping your pace slow. Use the following guidelines to make running a positive experience.

WALK FIRST
Start with three 30-minute walks a week for two to three weeks.

THEN RUN/WALK
Interspersing walk breaks into your running lets you catch your breath and protects your joints and muscles. "Even if you've run before, and especially if you're returning from an injury, walk breaks are smart," says running coach Jeff Galloway.

GO FOR TIME OVER DISTANCE
Runners love ticking off the miles, but don't worry about that at first. Running by time de-emphasizes pace, and allows you to adjust to how you feel that day.

TAP THE POWER OF THREE
"People who do not run regularly are more likely to quit," says Galloway. Run three days a week: You can only achieve running fitness if you do it consistently.

GET TO THE NINTH RUN
The end of the third week is the turning point for many new and returning runners. "Your metabolism's changed, you've got more energy, you've probably improved your diet—everything starts happening for you," says Anderson. "But you start to feel unfulfilled, so you need a new target."

ENDURANCE OVER SPEED
Fast running puts a greater demand on your muscles, connective tissues, and cardiovascular system. Build to 30 continuous minutes before you work on increasing speed.

3) MAKING IT STICK
AVOID THE GUILT OF MISSING A SESSION ANY WAY YOU CAN

SEEK PEER PRESSURE
Having a running date, whether it's with one person or a group, is a strong motivator. Ask about groups at your local running store, or check the forums at runnersworld.com.

RACE
A race is a great way to focus the mind and help runners plan ahead, says Holt. "You need to know what you are aiming for, whether it be to complete a race or simply to measure progress through your weight loss."

IMAGE: ALAMY

SET NEW TARGETS AS A REWARD.

REWARD YOURSELF

When you hit a milestone—that ninth run, running three days a week for a month, or completing your first race—give yourself a treat. "Whether it's the medal for finishing a race, a cupcake, or a trip to the Bahamas, it doesn't really matter. It is the carrot dangling at the end of the race that can help people achieve," says Holt. Rewards don't need to be physical, either. "We set new targets as a reward," says Anderson. "Once a runner has achieved their first target, they feel euphoric—'I've become a runner'—and want to do more."

ENLIST FAMILY

Support from your family and friends is vital if you're to keep it up. If you are being nagged by a partner every time you go for a run, it can soon become a chore, says Holt, but "most runners' families and friends can see the benefits in terms of both health and enjoyment." They may need a crash course when you start, though. "Educate your family so they understand what you do," says Anderson.

ADD VARIETY

A new route can enliven your running regimen. Find a trail, a different area to try, or if you normally run a loop, do it in reverse.

ACCEPT BAD RUNS

If you acknowledge that every run is not going to feel great, you will reduce your frustration. On tough days, slow your pace, take walk breaks, or shorten your run. "Runners think that once they've built up, they can't go back," says Galloway. "You can."

ACCENTUATE THE POSITIVE

McMillan wishes all new and returning runners would stop comparing themselves to others. "Don't put added pressure on yourself," says McMillan. "Instead, focus on the accomplishment of every workout."

FLEX PLAN Stretches for runners

It's likely that you'll wake up after your first run with sore, stiff muscles. You can minimize the "morning after" effect by walking for a few minutes and stretching after your run. As well as improving flexibility, it flushes the muscles with blood and oxygen, which promotes recovery. At the very least, focus on these three areas.

HAMSTRINGS

WHY They're your main propulsion muscles.
HOW Place your heel on a step or any elevated surface and bend slowly at the waist until you feel a stretch in the back of your thigh (you may also feel it in your calves). Avoid rounding your back. Hold for 30 to 60 seconds. Release and repeat four or five times. Switch sides.

CALVES

WHY They help propel you and absorb impact.
HOW Place both hands on a wall and take a step back with one leg. Keep your heel on the ground and lean into the wall until you feel a stretch. Hold and repeat four times. Switch sides. Repeat, but bend the knee of the extended leg slightly so you feel the stretch in the lower calf.

QUADS

WHY They are your legs' shock absorbers, controlling your movement every time you land.
HOW Stand up straight, bend one leg behind you, and grab your ankle; pull it toward your bottom and push the hip of the same leg forward until you feel the stretch in the front of your leg. Hold for 30 to 60 seconds. Release and repeat four times. Switch sides.

FITTING IT IN

You have the motivation to run but find you don't have the time—or so you think. These 25 tips will help you squeeze running into the busiest of schedules

> **WITH SO MUCH TO DO** in everyday life, from shopping to putting the children to bed, running can get squeezed out. Lack of time—whether actual or perceived—is the biggest barrier to getting in a run or running as much as you might like. We're here to help.

The way we see it, time problems fall into the three categories below: making time (questions of when, where, and how); saving time (little do's and don'ts that add up to serious savings); and rethinking time (adjusting the relationship between your running and the time you need to do it).

Here's the plan: Below are 25 time-management tips in these three categories. Pick any three of the strategies—one from each section—and try them for a month. If any work, great; if not, pick three more. If you try them all and still can't find time to run, you probably don't really want to. Which is a shame. Chances are, however, you'll find some that work every time. So stop making excuses and get your gear on!

>> MAKING TIME
YOU CAN DO IT FOR YOURSELF, AND ROPE IN A LITTLE HELP FROM THOSE AROUND YOU

1 PLAN YOUR WEEK
Sit down with your calendar on Sunday night and draw up a realistic training schedule, before the blank spaces start filling up with other priorities.

2 THINK QUALITY, NOT QUANTITY
Take the most out of what you have. Finding time for a 20-minute run is easy. Just make every minute count. Alternate one minute a little faster than your normal pace with one-minute recoveries. Do a two- to four-minute warmup first and a similar cooldown afterward.

3 GET UP 30 MINUTES EARLIER
Run before anyone else is even out of bed, because there are no appointments to get in the way of an early morning run, and it will invigorate you for the day ahead.

4 GET YOURSELF A DOG
There's no way to ignore a wet snout in your face telling you, "Now, now, NOW!" Having to exercise the dog will literally drag you out of the house.

5 SWAP YOUR DUTIES
One morning, afternoon, or evening, let your other half look after the children while you run. The next day, reverse the roles. Or…

6 TAKE THE KIDS WITH YOU
Many gyms now offer in-house day care. In 90 minutes, you can squeeze in an hour on the treadmill and a 20-minute circuit-training session on the weight machines—an excellent all-around workout that will improve strength and endurance. And your kids should get a bit of exercise in the bargain.

7 GIVE 'EM THE RUNAROUND
While the children are playing soccer (or whatever), run loops around the outside of the field. "I do this twice a week," says mother-of-two Judie Simpson. "Once as a steady one-hour run. The second time I'll pick it up on the long side of the field and jog the short side for 45 minutes or so."

8 BEAT THE RUSH HOUR
Take your gear to work and run home while everyone else is stuck in gridlock or squashed on a train. By the time you're home you'll be de-stressed from the rigors of the day and can allow yourself to feel ever so slightly smug.

IMAGE: ALAMY

BUDDY UP
Owning a dog gives
you no excuse to
stay indoors.

GETTING STARTED

9 SET SHORT-TERM GOALS

Too many runners think too far ahead—a six-month or yearlong plan—when laying out their training. "That vision can be lost pretty quickly when you're feeling bad," warns Dave Scott, six-time Ironman Hawaii winner. "Instead, set a shorter goal: Run three times a week for the next two weeks." Then set another, and so on.

10 PLACE YOUR BETS

People who bet $40 that they could stick with their training program for six months had a 97 percent success rate in a study at Michigan State University. Less than 20 percent of those who didn't place a bet stuck it out. Bet against a friend, and the first to give up pays up.

11 THINK LITTLE AND OFTEN

If you're new to it, aim for frequency, not duration, to make running a regular part of your life. Instead of trying to find time for a 45-minute run two or three times a week, do shorter sessions of 15 to 20 minutes, but run most days. A few small steps are more likely to keep you on your feet than one giant leap.

12 GO LONGER TO GET STRONGER

Veteran runners should focus on two "key" runs every week, sessions where they really push. Try a one-hour interval, fartlek, or hill run during the week and then a weekend long run. Fill in around them with short, easy runs, cross-training, and rest days. Two very tough runs will make you faster and stronger than five or six so-so weekly runs with little rest between them.

13 FIND A FRIEND

Recruit a regular training partner and agree on time, place, and distance. If someone is expecting you to show up, you're less likely to make excuses.

>> SAVING TIME
FIFTEEN SECONDS HERE, A MINUTE THERE. IT DOESN'T SEEM LIKE MUCH, BUT WATCH HOW FAST IT ALL ADDS UP

14 THINK AHEAD

Get your gear ready the night before. Even loosen your laces so your feet slide right into your shoes.

That way, you sit down and dress for battle quickly. No back-and-forth from bedroom to laundry and back to bedroom, tracking down something clean to wear.

15 GET READY FOR BREAKFAST

Plop your smoothie ingredients in a blender the night before an early morning run and put it in the fridge. After your run, hit the switch, and eight seconds later...breakfast is served. We tried this ourselves: Assembling from scratch in the morning took 1:53, meaning we saved a grand total of 1:45.

16 HOLD OFF ON THE STRETCHES

Don't spend time stretching cold muscles before you train. Instead, walk briskly for a few minutes, then start your run slowly.

17 RUN BEFORE YOU TALK

You meet your running partners and start talking while doing some lame trunk twists as a warmup. Don't do it. Say hello (it's only polite), and start running slowly. Talk then, before the pace picks up. Do all four of these tips from 14 to 17 and you'll save from seven to 10 minutes—enough time to turn your usual five-mile run into a six-miler. Over the course

IMAGE: ALAMY

FIND A PARTNER
You're less likely to make excuses when a friend is expecting you to show up.

of a workweek, you'll net at least 35 minutes of extra running time.

18 KEEP YOUR SHORTS ON

"Wear running shorts as underwear," says running guru Jeff Galloway, so you're run-ready the instant your antennae pick up a 10-minute block of free time. "Accumulate enough short runs and they add up," he says. A Stanford University study found that multiple bouts of moderate-intensity exercise produce significant training effects. Leading us to...

19 DIVIDE AND CONQUER

On busy days, beat the clock by breaking up your run into two shorter sessions. Instead of a single 40-minute run, maybe do 20 in the morning and the same at lunchtime, or whatever fits your schedule.

20 TURN DOWN THE VOLUME

Runners logging 50 miles a week had marathon times no faster than those who logged 40, in a study at the University of Northern Iowa. More isn't always better, so don't scramble to find time for miles simply to pad out your weekly total.

21 THE 10-MINUTE MIRACLE

"Run faster-than-normal training pace (but don't sprint) for 10 footfalls of your right foot. When you reach 10, do 10 more steps of easy running," says exercise physiologist Jack Daniels. Then do 20-20 and so on up to 60-60. Then work back to 10-10. This is a good way to warm up, cool down, and throw in some intensity in a short space of time.

>> RETHINKING TIME
SOME TIME BARRIERS TO RUNNING ARE EXTERNAL—WORK, PICKING UP THE CHILDREN, DOING THE FOOD SHOPPING, AND SO ON. BUT EQUALLY RESTRICTIVE ARE INTERNAL ROADBLOCKS—ATTITUDES TOWARD RUNNING AND/OR OURSELVES THAT STOP US FROM WORKING OUT

22 BE REALISTIC

Cut back on your running if you need to. But don't throw in the towel because life gets busy. Ride these periods out, and fit in a run of some kind—15 minutes, 10 minutes—every second or third day. Then resume a more intense routine when you can. When your schedule implodes, short-term changes can stop you from fretting your way into sofa sloth.

23 BE A BIT SELFISH

By giving your run a high priority, you boost your physical and emotional health, and live up to your obligation to your family to be healthy and happy.

24 BE FLEXIBLE

If circumstances change, don't make excuses. If a surprise meeting cancels the lunchtime run, do it after work. If you miss the alarm, take your gear to work and run at lunch. "If you really want to run, you'll find time," says former 2:09 marathoner Ron Hill. "It's really no different than finding time to shave, eat, or read the paper."

25 HAVE FUN!

Enjoying a run greatly increases the likelihood that you'll want to—and will—find time for the next one. Run a new route; run an old one backward. If you usually run on roads, head for the park and run through the trees. Variety really is the spice of life.

BE THE BLUR.

**MEB -
AMERICA'S #1
MARATHONER**

skechers
GOrun
3

Take your run to the next level in Skechers GOrun 3, featuring our award-winning midfoot strike technology and an all-new performance-engineered upper.

skechersperformance.com

IT'S GOOD TO WALK

There's no shame in adding a little walking to your running, says 1968 Boston Marathon winner Amby Burfoot

> **SHHHH.** I have a secret to share with you. You see, I used to be a fairly fast runner. In fact, I won the Boston Marathon at the age of 21. And there's a certain amount of honor among Boston winners—a sort of "pain is my friend" ethic—that we're sworn to uphold. Now, about that secret. I wouldn't want anyone to think I've gone soft or anything, but...this is hard to get out...I often take walking breaks during my daily runs.

There, that feels much better. Though I don't know why it was hard to say in the first place. After all, it makes perfect sense to mix running and walking. Think about it: When new runners start off, they often follow a run-walk routine; they run for maybe 30 seconds, walk until they feel recovered, then repeat the process for 20 to 30 minutes. This system has proven successful a thousand times over.

When world-class runners peak for the Olympics, they concentrate on "interval" training—the still-unsurpassed method for achieving maximum results. They run hard for one to five minutes, then walk or jog very slowly until they're ready to run hard again.

When ultradistance runners participate in those seemingly crazy races of 100 miles or more, they inevitably alternate running and walking. It's hard to imagine any other way to cover the mega-mile distances. You, on the other hand, probably view walking as the enemy. The thinking is that you run, and this is good. You are proving and improving yourself; you are determined; you are a moral person. Whereas when you walk, it is bad. You are lazy; you are a loser; you don't deserve to be loved (not even by your mother).

Mental-health therapists have many words for this sort of inflexible, perfectionist thinking, and I have

BIG STRIDES
Walking breaks can push your running to new heights.

IMAGE: ALAMY

GETTING STARTED

one, too. I call it "stupid." (None too elegant, but it has the benefit of clarity.) The goal of a session is not to avoid walking. The goals are to feel better, get in better shape, reduce tension, lose weight, train for an upcoming race, and so on. Take your pick. They're all worthwhile goals.

Run/walk training (R/W training) is a simple, commonsense approach to conditioning. It can help you train more (for better marathon preparation and calorie burning); it can help you train healthier (who needs injuries and burnout?); and it can even help you get faster (through interval training).

Enough talk. Let's be more specific.

THE GALLOWAY MARATHON

Olympic marathon runner Jeff Galloway has pioneered the idea of walking breaks during marathons. He advocates this program not only for many first-timers, but also for those who have previously hit the wall and experienced the crushing fatigue and depression of those last few miles. By walking early and often, Galloway has found, most runners survive the final miles in much better shape. They feel better, and often run faster as a result.

You can run/walk a marathon any way you want, but the simplest is to run the first mile, then walk for 60 seconds. Run the second mile, then walk for 60 seconds (and have a sports drink). Repeat 24 more times, then hold your head high and sprint like a hare.

The method has been used successfully by thousands of marathoners. Several have dipped below 3:30 this way, but fast times aren't the point. The point is that you can finish the marathon, feel good, run strong to the end, and admire that gleaming finisher's medal for the rest of your life.

THE NEXT STEP

The Galloway program has many converts, and I'm one of them. I've now run four marathons with walking breaks, in times ranging from 3:45 to 4:30. I'm a modest trainer these days, averaging 20 to 30 miles a week, so the marathon can easily intimidate me. A few years ago, I was beginning to dread the thought of running 26.2-milers. Now, I don't even think of the marathon that way. I think of it as a one-mile run that I just happen to repeat 26 times. Piece of cake.

R/W training has also made my daily training easier. It used to be that, much as I love running, I sometimes felt too tired to get through the door.

TOP TIPS

>> If you want to call yourself a runner, walking's out, isn't it? Not really. Running is good, but so is walking. It's a valid form of interval training employed even by elite runners.
>> R/W training can allow you to run longer, healthier, and, yes, faster—even on marathon day.

>> Try this marathon day plan: Run a mile, walk 60 seconds. Repeat 25 times until complete in good time and with no walls hit.
>> Incorporating walking into your routine reduces your chances of injury and assists injury recovery.
>> Ease the pain of those long runs with an R/W strategy that will deliver near-full endurance benefits.

I talked myself out of many sessions: When you're already tired, why drag yourself out on the roads for 40 minutes? I don't have this problem anymore, because I don't run for 40 minutes. I run for four minutes, then walk for a minute, then repeat the process until I've completed 40 minutes. All I care about is getting into the session and feeling energized afterward, which I always do.

A STEP BACKWARD

Let's pause for a moment to consider some of the differences between running and walking. Some are small, others more significant. Running and walking have much in common, with one big difference. Runners "jump" from foot to foot, walkers don't. When you run, the knee flexes more than in walking, the quadriceps contract, and you "toe-off" in more or less the same way as a long jumper leaps.

Because you toe-off and jump, you come down forcefully on the other foot. This is the "impact shock" of running—said to be two to three times your body weight—that can lead to overuse injuries. Walkers don't jump, so they are less likely to get injured.

Because you jump when running, you can cover ground much faster than a walker and burn many more calories per minute (because moving faster requires you to consume more oxygen). In other

IMAGE: ALAMY

words, you get a superior session in less time, which is one of the major benefits of running.

Unfortunately, many potential runners never get into the rhythm of running. They set out to run around the block a few times, but find themselves breathless at the first corner, so they retire to the sofa and never leave it again. These are the people who need to learn about R/W training. You won't get exhausted and frustrated (thanks to the walking breaks), and you'll get all the benefits that vigorous exercise brings (thanks to the running). There are many reasons for R/W training. Some are physical, some mental, but all will change (and probably improve) your running. Here are a few.

RUNNING FARTHER, EASIER All runners, from beginners to veterans, would like to run longer and easier. The R/W system gives you a new tool to help achieve this. Does it come at a cost? Sure. Your overall session is slower, so you get slightly less training effect, but most of the time you do long runs to build overall endurance and increase your body's ability to burn fat and calories in general.

INCREASED VARIETY Far too many runners do the same session at the same pace every time they run. It's boring, and it's not a smart way to train. An R/W session naturally has many small segments, which encourages you to experiment.

BETTER SPEEDWORK An R/W session is an offshoot of the classic interval session, so it's easy to make it a real gut-buster. Here's one of my favorites: Run easy for one minute, hard for two minutes, and easy for one minute. Then walk for one minute.

Repeat this eight times, and you've come reasonably close to the 8 x 400-meter torture my college coach loved to inflict on us.

On the topic of intervals, exercise physiologist Jack Daniels had two groups of women run three times a week, either continuously or with walking breaks. After 12 weeks, the run/walk group was more fit. Why? "In effect, the walking breaks turned the sessions into one big interval session," says Daniels. "It allowed the women to go faster overall."

FEWER INJURIES Walking doesn't cause as many injuries as running, so R/W training shouldn't either. Walking uses the leg muscles and connective tissues in a different way from running, so it should reduce overuse injuries. Walk with a slow, elongated stride to feel other muscles coming into play.

MORE SIGHTSEEING What's the point of running in some beautiful location if all you see are the rocks and gnarly roots on the trail in front of you? Yet that's all many trail runners see, because they're concentrating so hard on avoiding falls and twisted ankles. With R/W you can drink in the views during your walking breaks.

MORE EFFECTIVE RECOVERY DAYS Some days you need to run slow, particularly if you ran long or fast the previous day, or if you're busy at work or home.

FASTER COMEBACKS You've had a sore knee, a bad Achilles, or a nasty cold. You're ready to get back into your training routine but don't want to overdo it and suffer a setback. Listen to your body, and don't run farther or faster than what feels right.

FINAL THOUGHTS

The aspect of R/W training I find most appealing—the mental breaks provided by the brief walking periods—won't prove equally compelling to all runners. Many will staunchly resist. "I didn't start running to become a walker," they'll snort derisively. Old habits die hard, and R/W training isn't for everyone. Or for every session. I do it a couple of times a week, usually when I run by myself and often as a long run.

However—and this is the most surprising thing about it—I've found that it has motivated me to do more speedwork. In fact, you could say that R/W training is classic interval training that's been liberated from the track and allowed to roam wherever you want to take it. You just might discover an entirely new, enjoyable (and effective) way to run. It's worth a try, isn't it?

A SHOE THING

There's no such thing as the "best shoe"—everybody has different needs. Biomechanics, body weight, the surfaces you run on, your injury history, and the structure and function of your feet mean one person's ideal is someone else's nightmare. Here's how to avoid the pitfalls.

> **FOR NEARLY THREE DECADES**, we organized shoes and reviews into categories: motion-control, stability, neutral-cushioned, and performance-training. The format was rooted in the prevailing science, which held that flat-footed runners needed stability features, high-arched runners just needed cushioning, and everyone else fell somewhere in between. But that model has grown outdated. As designs got more creative and features crossed category lines, it became hard to distinguish between, say, a neutral-cushioned shoe and a stability shoe. Focusing on these categories—rather than on you, the runner—was making less and less sense.

Runner's World now positions shoes along a spectrum ranging from shoes that offer more protection to those that offer less. At one end, shoes with more stability features and cushioning offer the most protection, but are heavier, less flexible, and higher off the ground. At the other end, you'll find more performance-oriented footwear: racing flats and minimal shoes are lightweight, flexible, and low profile, but offer very little protection. The shoes in between offer a balance of protective and performance features in different combinations.

How much protection do you need? Your risk of injury depends on age, experience, body weight, anatomy, mileage, and other factors. The more injury risk factors you have, the more protection you need. Novice, older, and heavier runners, and those with a history of injury are more at risk and need more protection. The height and flexibility of your arch, and how much you pronate (see "Shoepedia," below) can help determine how much stability you need from a shoe. More experienced, lightweight, and injury-free runners tend to prefer lighter, more flexible footwear with few, if any, motion-controlling features.

The first step in finding your ideal shoe is to take our "wet test" (see page 21). This works on the basis that the shape of your wet footprint roughly correlates with the amount of stability you might need in your shoe. "Roughly" is the key word here, though: It's a handy starting point, but no more than that.

Second, determine a range of shoes that offer you the appropriate level of protection. Our Shoe Finder tool (runnersworld.com/shoefinder) will help you identify a handful of specific models that work for runners with your biomechanical profile and running habits.

Once you've done that, and have at least some idea of shoes that may best suit you, visit your local specialty running shop for a professional fitting.

ONE FIT NEVER FITS ALL

With the right advice, most runners will be able to find a shoe that's right for them. Once you've determined how much protection you need from a shoe, you have a wide range of options to choose from. All you have to do is decide which shoe within the range provides the best comfort and fit for your needs. Try out a handful of different models, listen to the advice, and don't rush into a decision if you're unsure.

Some people have problems finding a comfortable shoe. A minority of runners have very specific needs, which can make shoe-buying a frustrating business. On the next page we will outline the most common biomechanical problems, such as heel-striking, underpronation, and so on. All will be explained in due course—to help you get ready... set...to go shopping.

SHOEPEDIA An A–Z of running-shoe jargon

Making your first trip to your local specialty running store to choose a pair of shoes can be a daunting prospect. A reputable shop will always try to make sure they sell you the best shoes for you, rather than the most expensive ones, but in order to understand your needs, you have to be able to communicate them. Check out our jargon-busting guide to the technical talk before you make your purchase.

BAREFOOT
A truly bare foot, without any type of covering or protection. See "minimal shoe" for the next step up in footwear

BIOMECHANICALLY EFFICIENT
A runner with few anatomical risk factors, a smooth and economical stride, and average pronation—no excessive inward or outward rolling. Does not need added stability features in a shoe. Also called "neutral" or "efficient."

BLOWN RUBBER
The lightest, most-cushioned, and least-durable form of rubber on the outsole. Made by injecting air into the rubber.

CARBON RUBBER
A harder, more durable outsole, made from solid rubber with carbon additives.

COLLAR
Made out of a soft material, the collar should wrap just below the ankle and supply a snug, gap-free fit. **»**

IMAGE: RODALE STUDIO

GETTING STARTED

IF YOU'RE A FOREFOOT-STRIKER...

YOU... land and push off from your toes when you run, rather than following the more typical pattern of landing on the outside edge of your heel and rolling through to push off from your toes.

YOU NEED SHOES THAT... have excellent forefoot cushioning, flexibility, and stability. However, you need to have an expert assess precisely why you're a forefoot-striker. If it's because you have a high arch and a rigid ankle, you need a neutral shoe to encourage foot motion, with a flexible forefoot.

If you're a forefoot-striker simply because you have tight calves, you should address this problem with stretching and/or physical therapy rather than trying to compensate via your shoes.

Finally, some runners favor the forefoot simply because they run quickly; they need light, responsive shoes, with an emphasis on forefoot cushioning and stability.

IF YOU'RE AN EXTREME HEEL-STRIKER...

YOU... prematurely destroy the outsole rubber (and probably the cushioning) on the outside heel of your shoes. This is usually because you land in an exaggerated way, though if you're heavy, that could also contribute.

YOU NEED SHOES THAT... have thick, durable outsoles and resilient midsole foam. Because the composition of the outsole compound is at least as important as its thickness, you need to know about a shoe's reputation before you buy. Ask your local specialty retailer, or check out runnersworld.com for the latest shoe reviews.

IF YOU UNDERPRONATE...

YOUR... feet and ankles don't roll inward enough when you run, a movement that would normally help absorb shock every time your feet strike the ground. This is a rare condition, and certainly less common than excessive roll (overpronation), but there are shoes to help overcome the problem.

YOU NEED SHOES THAT... encourage the inward movement of the foot (pronation). Look for a shoe with soft midsole cushioning. Avoid shoes with added stability features, such as medial posts. These are firm sections on the arch side of the midsole, designed to limit lateral movement for those runners who overpronate.

SHOEPEDIA An A–Z of running-shoe jargon *(continued)*

>> CUSHIONING

The materials in the sole of a running shoe that soften impact and distribute the pressure of the foot. For most runners, the amount of cushioning required is a personal preference, but heavier runners tend to do better with firmer cushioning. Softer soles work better for lightweight runners.

DROP

The difference, in millimeters, between the stack heights of the heel and forefoot. The average running shoe has a 12 mm drop; minimal footwear has a smaller difference.

DUAL-DENSITY MIDSOLE

A mechanism, usually a firmer wedge of foam on the medial (inner) side of the shoe, used to correct overpronation.

EYELETS

The laces run through these to tighten the shoe. If you feel pressure under a particular pair of eyelets, you don't have to use those to tie your shoe.

FLEX GROOVES

Indentations molded into the midsole and outsole to make a shoe more flexible.

FLEXIBILITY

The ability of a shoe's forefoot to bend under the ball of the foot. If the shoe does not flex easily under your weight, your foot and leg muscles have to work harder, which saps energy and can cause injuries such as shinsplints.

FOREFOOT

The broad, front section of the shoe or foot. This is the point from which you propel yourself forward, so the shoe should be protective yet responsive. Some runners land on the fronts of their feet (they're called forefoot-strikers) and need maximum cushioning in the forefoot of their shoes.

GAIT CYCLE

The body's movement from step to step, including the foot's transition through to toe-off. Heel-strikers make initial contact with the ground at the outer part of the heel. The foot then rolls forward and inward (pronates) as the arch collapses to absorb shock. Then it moves on to the inner and front part of the forefoot as the foot stiffens and pushes away from the ground (toe-off). Some faster, lighter runners make flat footed (or "midfoot") contact with the ground, usually on the outside edge of the foot. A minority of runners contact the ground forefoot first.

DO YOUR HOMEWORK AND DON'T RUSH INTO A DECISION.

IF YOU WEAR ORTHOTICS...

YOU... have custom-made insoles designed to correct biomechanical imbalances. They are usually—but not always—built to provide additional stability.

YOU NEED SHOES THAT... fit your orthotics, and work with them in the way that your podiatrist intended. Usually, if your orthotics provide all the correction you need, your podiatrist is likely to recommend using them in a neutral but supportive shoe. Extreme overpronators may be recommended a motion-control shoe, especially since, in the view of many leading podiatrists, the chance of having too much stability is slim.

In either case, look for shoes that are roomy enough to accommodate orthotics comfortably. Look particularly for a deep heel counter, as built-up orthotics can compromise stability and comfort in shallow-fitting shoes.

THE WET TEST

Dip the bottom of your foot in water, step straight onto a brown paper bag, and match the imprint with the arch types below.

HIGH, RIGID ARCHES need more impact protection and are best suited to cushioned shoes without stability features.

AVERAGE ARCH runners can wear just about any running shoe, depending on other risk factors.

LOW, FLEXIBLE ARCHES are often found on overpronating runners. They should wear shoes with stability features.

HEEL COUNTER
An internal support feature in the rear of the shoe that sits around your heel and usually has a notch cut in the top to avoid irritating the Achilles tendon. The fit of the shoe isn't perfect unless the heel sits flush against this stiff backing. Tapping the foot back into the heel will lock it into position.

INSOLE
The foot-shaped insert, usually removable, that sits between your foot and the shoe. Also known as a "sockliner."

LACES
Used to pull the upper around the arch. If you can feel your laces, either they or the tongue are too thin.

LATERAL
The outside (little toe) edge.

LUGS
Deep, rubber tread on the underside of the shoe to provide grip in off-road conditions.

MEDIAL
The inside (big toe and arch) edge.

MEDIAL POST
A firmer density of foam, sometimes with an additional plastic device, inserted into the rear, arch-side section of the midsole to add support or control excessive rear motion.

MIDSOLE
The material (usually EVA or polyurethane foam) that sits below the upper and above the outsole, protecting you from impact and often encasing other technologies, such as gel pouches or air pockets, for extra durability and protection.

MINIMAL SHOE
Lightweight, flexible shoes with a rubber outsole for traction and abrasion resistance and a simple upper but not much else. These usually feature little, if any, cushioning.

OUTSOLE
The durable part of the shoe that makes contact with the ground, providing traction.

OVERLAYS
These leather strips over the top of the upper work with the laces and eyelets to make the shoe conform to the shape of the foot.

OVERPRONATION
Excessive inward rolling of the foot, which prevents normal toe-off and can expose you to a host of injury problems, particularly in the knees. ➤➤

IF YOU HAVE WIDE FEET...

YOU... are not alone. As more runners get medical advice and gait analysis, more manufacturers now offer a growing range of shoes to cater to the specific needs of those with wide feet.

YOU NEED SHOES THAT... keep pressure off the sides of your feet, and allow the recommended thumb's width of space between your longest toe and the end of the shoe.

Beware, though. Finding the right shoe isn't simply a matter of reaching for the nearest available option in a wide fit. It actually depends on why your feet are wide relative to their length (it also has to meet your stability and cushioning needs). If you have short toes, you'll need a shoe that flexes further forward than normal because relatively speaking, that's what your feet do. Your retailer will look for the position of the flex grooves on the underside of the shoe to help you avoid a retail blunder here.

IF YOU HAVE NARROW FEET...

YOU... need to do more than just lace up normal shoes tightly.

YOU NEED SHOES THAT... don't allow your feet to slip around inside. Not only will over-wide shoes feel less responsive, you'll also be more at risk of blisters in the areas where your feet do touch the shoe, because you'll be sliding around. As with the wider fits, most manufacturers have woken up to the fact that not everyone has standard-sized or standard-shaped feet, and they now offer narrow options.

TOP TIP

LOOP-LACING LOCK

This is a great way for anyone to create a secure, tight fit. Just put each lace end back into the same hole it just exited, leaving a small loop on the top side of the shoe; now thread each loose end through the loop on the opposite side; then pull to create a supertight closure.

PROBLEM NARROW FOOT
SOLUTION Using the loop-lacing lock halfway up the shoe doubles the laces over your midfoot, ensuring a tight fit.

PROBLEM HEEL SLIPPING IN YOUR SHOE
SOLUTION Lace the shoe using the normal crisscross technique, then tie a loop-lacing lock on the last eyelet.

PROBLEM HIGH INSTEP
SOLUTION Start with normal crisscross lacing, but over the midfoot feed the laces up each side of the shoe. Finish with the crisscross technique at the top.

PROBLEM WIDE FOREFOOT
SOLUTION Over the width of your foot just feed the laces up each side of the shoe, again using the crisscross technique at the top.

SHOEPEDIA An A-Z of running-shoe jargon (continued)

>> PRONATION
The inward rolling of the foot, which is a natural part of the gait cycle.

STACK HEIGHT
The measurement in millimeters that your heel or forefoot sits from the ground. This includes everything under your foot—rubber outsole, foam midsole, sockliner, etc.

SUPINATION
Opposite of overpronation, the foot rolls outward on impact and needs to be corrected with appropriate footwear.

TOEBOX
The front part of the fabric upper surrounding the toes.

TOE-OFF
Final stage of the gait cycle, which propels you forward as your foot pushes off from the ground.

TONGUE
The tongue should be pulled up tight and lined up straight. You should use a tongue's lace keeper to hold it in place.

UNDERPRONATION
Too little inward rolling of the foot to dissipate the force of the footstrike.

UPPER
The top fabric section that holds the laces.

VAMP
A part of the upper that surrounds the toebox. If you can pinch a quarter inch, the vamp is too loose. If you can't wiggle your toes, it's too tight.

running forever changed

1 Durable Techfit Upper
Reduces weight and wraps seamlessly around the foot to form an ultra flexible second skin

2 Elastic Open Pore Mesh
Adapts to different foot shapes and keeps feet cooler

3 Protective External Heel Counter
Keeps the foot 'locked-in' and increases stability

4 Energy Capsules
Thousands of unique energy storing capsules store and return the energy other midsoles lose

5 Minimalist and Lightweight
BOOST™ allows for a more minimalistic shoe construction, the build is lightweight, natural to your foot and low to the ground

6 Torsion® System
Allows the fore and rear-foot to move independently for a smoother transition

GET YOUR GEAR ON

You've got the shoes. Here's what else to look for—and why

T-SHIRTS

THE BEST ONES HAVE...

> Flat seams for comfort
> Wicking material to transfer away sweat
> A UV-protective coating for running in the sun
> Anti-odor technology

SHORTS

THE BEST ONES HAVE...

> An elastic waistband for comfort
> Fluorescent piping for night running
> Small pocket for keys, ID, and so on
> A liner inside to hold everything in place

JACKETS

THE BEST ONES HAVE...

> Adjustable waistband and cuffs
> Strong weather-resistant material
> Soft, nonrubbing fabric
> An ergonomic design

LEGGINGS

THE BEST ONES HAVE...

> An elastic waistband for comfort
> Fluorescent piping for night running
> Small pocket for keys, ID, and so on
> Paneling for an ergonomic fit

SOCKS

THE BEST ONES HAVE...

> Elastic arch lock
> Padded soles
> Seam-free toe section
> Breathable, anti-chafe material

49 REASONS TO LOVE RUNNING

You shouldn't need an excuse to get out there, but there are plenty of very good reasons to slip those shoes on right now

1 SAY GOODBYE TO YOUR BELLY

Dublin University researchers report that a 140-pound adult burns 391 calories in 30 minutes of running, compared with 277 calories while cycling, and 272 calories while playing tennis. Translation? You blitz your belly up to 40 percent faster.

2 BULLETPROOF BONES

Fifteen minutes of light jogging three times a week is all it takes to reduce your risk of developing osteoporosis in later life by up to 40 percent, according to the National Osteoporosis Society.

3 HIT THE MARK

Some runners set distance or time goals; many focus on health or weight. Others run simply to relax. It can help you achieve any goal you set your mind to.

4 IT'S THE ALL-WEATHER ACTIVITY

Rain, cold, sun, wind—there's no excuse not to get out there. Just strip off or layer up and see it as another challenge.

5 GET H-A-P-P-Y

"Mild to moderate exercise releases natural feel-good endorphins that help counter stress and literally make you happy," explains Andrew McCulloch, chief executive of the Mental Health Foundation in the United Kingdom.

6 TAKE OVER THE WORLD!

Early-morning runs present truly beautiful experiences worth cherishing—while the rest of the world sleeps, you're the first to break the virgin snow over that field, the deserted streets are yours and yours alone, you see the glory of the sunrise and you don't have to share it with anyone. How smug do you feel?

7 JOIN THE ZZZ-LIST

Stanford University School of Medicine researchers asked sedentary insomnia sufferers to jog for just 20 to 30 minutes every other day. The result? The time required to fall asleep was reduced by half, and sleep time increased by almost one hour.

8 MEDALS ARE COOL

Silverware isn't just for Olympians. Enter a race, finish it, and you'll have your own to line up on your mantelpiece as proof of what you've managed to achieve.

9 ENJOY GUILT-FREE SNACKING

Upping your salt intake is seldom a doctor's advice, but in the last few days before a marathon that's exactly what you should do—giving you the perfect excuse to munch on potato chips. The salt in them helps protect against hyponatremia, a condition caused by drinking too much water without enough sodium, which can lead to disorientation, illness, and, in rare cases, death.

ILLUSTRATIONS: JOHN UELAND

GETTING STARTED

10 KEEP THE DOCTOR AT BAY

"Moderate exercise makes immune cells more active, so they're ready to fight off infection," says Cath Collins, chief dietitian at St. George's Hospital in London. In studies at the University of North Carolina, people who jogged for 15 minutes five days a week took half as many sick days as couch potatoes.

11 GET REGULAR

According to experts from Bristol University, the benefits of running extend right to your bottom. "Physical activity helps decrease the time it takes food to move through the large intestine, thus limiting the amount of water absorbed back into your body, leaving you with softer stools that are easier to pass," explains gastroenterologist Ken Heaton, M.D.

12 SEE THE WORLD

What other sport is there where you get the chance to travel to all four corners of the earth in the name of fitness? From the New York to Rio de Janeiro marathons all the way to seeing parts of your own country that you never even knew existed, it's a veritable ticket to ride.

13 YOU DON'T NEED AN INSTRUCTION MANUAL

If you can walk, you can run. Think back to being a child, and you will realize that running is one of the most natural instincts to humankind.

14 PROTECT YOUR TICKER

Studies from Purdue University have shown that regular running can cut your risk of heart disease by 50 percent.

15 GET TIME BACK ON YOUR SIDE

Whether loosely lodged in your mental schedule or typed into your BlackBerry, your daily workout should be a focal point of your day. It helps you organize everything else you need to do, often into B.R. (Before Run) and A.R. (After Run) time frames, as well as giving you time to absorb and ponder your daily itinerary.

16 REACH CREATIVE BREAKTHROUGHS

Writers, musicians, artists, and many other creative professionals use running to solve mental blocks and make must-do-it-today decisions. For this we can credit the flow of oxygen to your gray matter when it matters most, sparking your brain's neurons and giving you breathing space away from the muddle of "real life."

17 THINK FASTER

Researchers from University of Illinois found that an improvement of only five percent in cardio-respiratory fitness from running led to an improvement of up to 15 percent on mental tests.

18 YOU CAN BE AN ALL-AROUNDER

Whether you want to keep in prime shape like Formula One champion Jenson Button, or go 12 hard rounds like boxer Amir Khan, running is the place to begin.

19 HILLS: THE ULTIMATE CALORIE-KILLER

Find a decent incline, take a deep breath (at the bottom, not the top), and incorporate it into your running program. You'll burn up to 40 percent more calories—the average 150-pound runner will burn 1,299 calories running a 10 percent incline for an hour, compared with 922 on the flat.

20 MAKE A DIFFERENCE

Millions of runners worldwide turn their determination to get fitter and healthier into fund-raising efforts for the less fortunate. The Flora London Marathon is the single largest annual fund-raising event in the world, having brought more than $643 million into the coffers of good causes to date. If that doesn't give you a warm glow, what will?

21 BOOST YOUR SEX LIFE

A study from Cornell University concluded that male runners have the sexual prowess of men two to five years younger, while females can delay menopause by a similar amount of time. Meanwhile, research conducted at Harvard University found that men over 50 who run at least three hours a week have a 30 percent lower risk of impotence than those who do little or no exercise.

the dog for a walk. Suddenly every journey has a double purpose—and, most important, one you'll love.

24 THAT NEW-SHOE SMELL

You've read the reviews in *Runner's World* (haven't you?), chatted with fellow runners, tried on and sampled your top three, and made your choice. Now they're here, in your hands. It's the start of a beautiful relationship.

25 THE JOY OF FINDING A NEW ROUTE

Today you took a left rather than a right and suddenly found amazing views and a piece of solitude you never knew existed before now. Then you imagine how many more runs there are out there just waiting to be discovered.

26 THAT KNOWING NOD FROM A FELLOW COMPETITOR

The race is about to start, and you see the same face from the last meet. Out of mutual respect and an acknowledgement of the challenge to come, you both nod. Nobody else knows it, but the gauntlet has been thrown down.

27 INDULGE YOUR WANDERLUST

There's simply no better way of getting to know a new city than putting on your running shoes and hitting the streets. Besides giving you necessary orientation, it'll energize you after your journey, reset your biological clock to any new time zone, and give you the chance to meet locals in half the time.

28 GET (A LEGAL) HIGH

Comparing the prerun and postrun scans of runners, neurologists from the University of Bonn, Germany, found evidence of more opiate binding of the happy hormone endorphin in the frontal and limbic regions of the brain, areas known to be involved in processing emotions and stress.

29 YOU'VE GOT A REAL FRIEND

We all go through phases in our lives, including times when we run less. You may get a job that demands more of your time. You may have to spend more time having and caring for a new baby. Maybe you simply go on vacation or take a sabbatical. That's fine.

22 IT CAN REPLACE A HARMFUL DEPENDENCY

...such as smoking, alcoholism, or overeating, says William Glasser, author of *Positive Addiction*. Result: You're a happier, healthier person getting the kind of fix that adds to, rather than detracts from, the good things in life.

23 END BOREDOM

The most mundane errand can be transformed into a training run, from buying a carton of milk to taking

GETTING STARTED

Running adapts itself easily to your ebbs and flows. Best of all, running is always there to take the strain when you need it most.

30 NUMBERS DON'T LIE

There's no leeway for dishonesty with running, from distances to times. You get back what you put in.

31 A RUNNING CLUB CAN SAVE YOUR LIFE

A nine-year study from Harvard Medical School found those with the most friends cut their risk of death by more than 60 percent, reducing blood pressure and strengthening their immune system.

32 BLITZ BODY BLEMISHES

"Running tones the buttocks and thighs quicker than any other exercise, which literally squeezes out the lingering fat," according to Dr. James Fleming, author of *Beat Cellulite Forever*.

33 BOOST YOUR BELLOWS

When running, an adult uses about 10 times the oxygen they would need when sitting in front of the television for the same period. Over time, regular jogging will strengthen the cardiovascular system, enabling your heart and lungs to work more efficiently, getting more oxygen where it's needed, quicker. This means you can do more exercise for less effort. How good does that sound?

34 BURN MORE FAT

"Even after running for 20 minutes or half an hour, you could be burning a higher amount of total calories for a few hours after you stop," says sports physiologist Mark Simpson of Loughborough University's School of Sports Science in the United Kingdom.

35 APPRECIATE THE ENVIRONMENT

You crave fresh, clean air when you run. You long for soft trails, towering trees, pure water. You have plenty of time to ponder the big questions. You resolve: Save the earth. You've got a vested interest.

36 THAT PR FEELING

Note the "p" here, being "personal"—you set the goals, you put the work in, you get the results. Savor it.

37 SPEND QUALITY TIME AS A FAMILY

It's one of the few activities that the whole family can do together. The smallest tyke can clamber into her jogging stroller, fit parents and grandparents can take turns pushing, and Junior can follow along on his new two-wheeler. Hundreds of races include events for everyone in the family.

39 TEACH YOURSELF DISCIPLINE

Practice makes perfect, in running and in life. The most successful people are the ones with a modest amount of talent and a huge amount of discipline.

40 IT'S NOT ELITIST

You're struggling in last place in the race but get the biggest cheer. You deserve it. After all, you've been running for longer than anyone else. What other sports are there where the laggards are applauded as much as the winners? Running's there for everyone, regardless of talent.

41 SIZE DOESN'T MATTER

Running is a great activity for every body type. There are no barriers to giving it a try.

42 YOU'RE IN CONTROL

Whatever the pressures of your job or personal life, you have the final say in how much or how little running you do. Squeeze in a predawn blast, a lunchtime refresher, or an evening stress-buster. It's your call.

43 HELP BABY

Moms-to-be who regularly exercise during pregnancy have an easier, less complicated labor, a quicker recovery, and better overall mood throughout the nine months, say researchers at Central Michigan University. Just ask Paula Radcliffe.

44 EXCUSE FOR A MASSAGE

Postrace, nothing quite beats the indulgence of a massage and the relaxed, floaty feeling as you walk back to real life.

45 YOUR PERSONAL THERAPIST

There's no greater escape from the pressures and stresses of modern life than slipping on your running shoes and just getting out there. It's just you and the road—giving you time to organize your life, think things through, and invariably finish in a better place than when you set off.

46 YOU CAN KEEP ON GOING FOREVER

While other sports have a limited shelf life, runners don't have to throw in the towel. Just look at 75-year-old legend Ron Hill, who hasn't missed a day's running since December 1964.

38 OUTRUN THE REAPER

Kings College London researchers compared more than 2,400 identical twins and found that those who did the equivalent of just three 30-minute jogs a week were nine years "biologically younger," even after discounting other influences including body mass index (BMI) and smoking.

GETTING STARTED

47 TAKE A JOURNEY

You never know what you'll find. You don't know whom or what you'll see. Even more interesting, who knows what thoughts might flash into your mind. Today's run could change your life in a way that you could never have imagined when you laced up your shoes.

48 IRON OUT THE CREASES

Regular running can reduce the signs of aging. "Increased circulation delivers oxygen and nutrients to skin cells more effectively, while flushing harmful toxins out," explains dermatologist Christopher Rowland Payne. "Exercise creates the ideal environment within the body to optimize collagen production to support the skin, helping reduce the appearance of wrinkles."

49 IT'S FREE

All you need are shoes, shorts, and a shirt.

DESIGNED FOR FREEDOM

Our goal is to inspire runners to go beyond pavement and enjoy greater freedom to run anywhere, regardless of where they start and finish. The result is lightweight, athlete-driven gear for the most liberated running experiences. See more at salomon.com/door2trail

COPYRIGHT © SALOMON SAS. ALL RIGHTS RESERVED. PHOTOGRAPHER: SCOTT MARKEWITZ. LOCATION: MARIN HEADLANDS, CALIFORNIA.

salomon

THE 12 TRAINING ESSENTIALS

Running doesn't have to be complicated: Arm yourself with some basic knowledge and you can start training with confidence. Here's how to make it through your first effort with flying colors

1 WELCOME TO THE STARTING LINE

This might be your first try at running, or a return visit, or an attempt to improve on what you already do. The less running you've done recently, the more you can expect to improve your distances and speeds in the first 10 weeks. On the other hand, the less you've run lately, the more likely you are to hurt yourself by doing too much, too soon. That's why it's so important to set two related goals as you start or restart your running program—to maximize improvements and to minimize injuries.

2 MAKE A PLAN

As for finding places to run, anywhere that's safe for walking is also fine for running. Off-road routes (parks, bike paths, playing fields) are better than busy streets, while soft surfaces (grass and dirt) are better than paved ones, but any choice is better than staying at home. Map out the best courses in your immediate neighborhood. That saves time, solves the "place" issue, and makes it much more likely you'll execute your planned runs.

3 EAT AND DRINK THE RIGHT FOODS

Sports nutrition is a big topic, but, in general, the rules for good nutrition and fluid consumption are the same for runners as for everyone else. Three

areas of special interest to runners: (1) control your weight, as extra pounds will slow you down; (2) eat lightly after training and racing; (3) drink 8 to 16 ounces of water or a sports drink an hour before running, as dehydration can be a dangerous enemy.

4 GET F.I.T.

Kenneth Cooper, a giant in the fitness field, long ago devised a simple formula for improving as a runner. Run two to three miles, three to five days a week, at a comfortable pace. It's easier to remember as the F.I.T. formula: frequency (at least every other day), intensity (comfortable pace), and time (about 30 minutes). Even with some walking breaks thrown in if you tire, you can cover two miles in 30 minutes, and you might soon be running three miles in that time. It's important to run these efforts at an easy, comfortable pace. Think of yourself as the Tortoise, not the Hare. Make haste slowly.

5 FIND YOUR PACE

We've told you to make it comfortable, which sounds simple. But the problem is that most novice runners don't actually know what a comfortable pace feels like, so they push too hard. As a result, they get overly fatigued and discouraged, or even injured, so either give up almost before they've started or face an injury layoff.

FIND YOUR PACE
Follow these tips
and you'll find your
comfort zone.

IMAGE: ALAMY

Here are some more guidelines: A comfortable pace is one to two minutes per mile slower than your optimum mile time. Or you can use a heart-rate monitor and run at 65 percent of your working heart rate. Finally, as an alternative, listen to your breathing. If you aren't gasping for air, and you can talk while you're running, your pace is about right.

6 REMEMBER TO WARM UP AND COOL DOWN FIRST

Don't confuse a little light stretching with a good warmup. Stretching exercises generally don't make you sweat or raise your heart rate, which is what you really want from a warmup. A proper warmup begins with walking or running very slowly to ease your body into the session. Try walking briskly for five minutes (about a quarter of a mile), and then breaking into your comfortable running pace. (Don't count the warmup as part of your run time or distance—that's cheating.)

When you finish your run, resist the urge to stop. Instead, walk another five minutes to cool down

more gradually. After you've cooled down is the best time for stretching—when your muscles are warm and ready to be stretched a little.

7 RUN SAFELY AT ALL TIMES

The biggest threat you'll face as a runner on the road, by far, is traffic. Cars, trucks, and bikes zip past you. A moment's lapse in attention from either you or them can result in, at the very least, a bad case of road rage. The best way to lower this risk is to avoid running near roads, but for many of us this is a near impossibility, or it's an approach that adds time and complexity to our routine (if we have to drive to a park, for example).

So most of us adapt and learn to be extremely cautious on the roads. Try to find quiet roads with wide shoulders or sidewalks; if there is no sidewalk, run on the left side of the road, facing the oncoming traffic; obey traffic signs and signals; and follow every road rule your parents taught you. If you look out for cars, trucks, and bikes, they won't have to look out for you.

8 USE PAIN AS YOUR GUIDE

Runners get hurt. We rarely hurt ourselves as seriously as skiers or football players, but injuries do happen. Most are musculoskeletal, meaning we recover rapidly when we take days off or other appropriate action (such as ice treatment), and most are self-inflicted—we bring them on by running too far, too fast, too soon, or too often.

Prevention is often as simple as a change of routine. If you can't run steadily without pain, mix walking and running. If you can't run-walk, simply walk. If you can't walk, cycle. If you can't cycle, swim. As you recover, climb back up this fitness ladder until you can run again.

9 TAKE THE MILE TRIAL

Friends who hear that you've begun running will soon ask what your best mile time is—so you might as well get used to it. Before long, you'll be calculating your pace per mile on longer runs, but you should begin with a simple one-mile test run (four laps on a standard track) to determine your starting point. Think of this run as a pace test, not a race. Run at a pace a little beyond easy, but less than a struggle, and count on improving your mile time in later tests as your fitness improves.

10 INCLUDE STRETCHING AND STRENGTHENING

Running is a specialized activity, working mainly the legs. If you're seeking total-body fitness, you need to supplement your running with other exercises. These should aim to strengthen the muscles that running neglects, and stretch those that running tightens, which means strengthening the upper body and stretching the legs. Add a few minutes of strengthening and stretching after your runs, because that's when these exercises tend to have the greatest benefit.

11 FOLLOW THE HARD DAY/EASY DAY TRAINING SYSTEM

Most runs need to be easy. This is true whether you're a beginner or an elite athlete. (Of course, the definition of easy varies hugely; an easy mile for an elite runner would be impossible for many beginners or even experienced runners.) As a new runner, make sure you limit yourself to one hard day a week. Run longer and slower than normal, or shorter and faster than normal, or enter a short (5-K) race and maintain your best pace for the entire distance.

STRETCH YOURSELF
Stretching after a run is better than doing it before you set off.

12 CONGRATULATE YOURSELF

One of the great beauties of running is that it gives everyone a chance to win. Winning isn't automatic; you still have to work for success and risk failure, but in running, unlike in other sports, there's no need to beat an opponent or an arbitrary standard (such as "par" in golf). Runners measure themselves against their own standards.

When you improve a time or increase a distance, or set a personal best in a race, you win—no matter what anyone else has done on the same day. You can win even more simply by keeping at it for the long haul, for years and decades. You don't have to run very far or fast to outrun people who have dropped out. It's the Tortoise and the Hare all over again. Slow and steady always wins the most important race.

IMAGE: EMBRY RUCKER

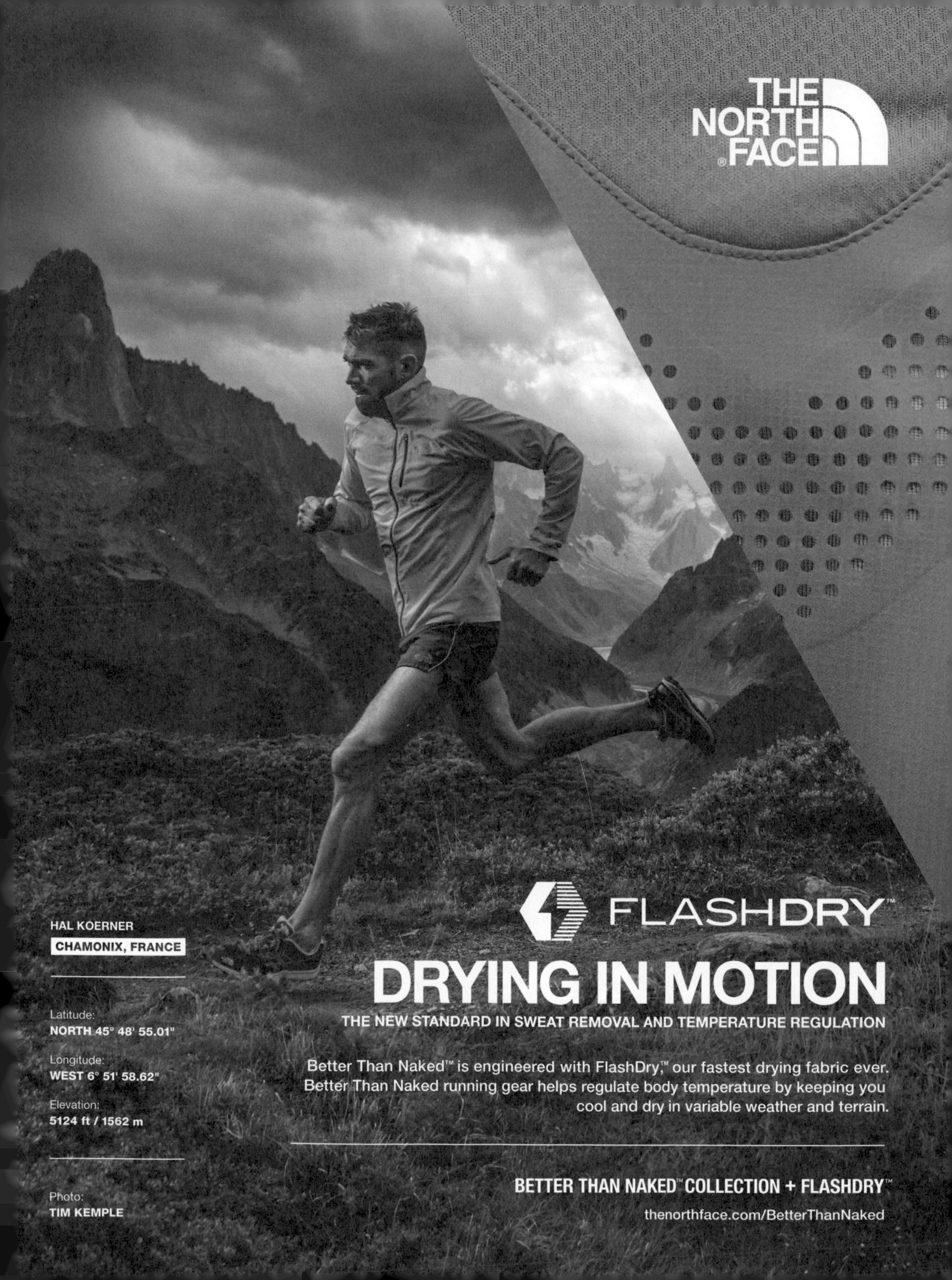

THE NORTH FACE®

HAL KOERNER
CHAMONIX, FRANCE

Latitude:
NORTH 45° 48' 55.01"

Longitude:
WEST 6° 51' 58.62"

Elevation:
5124 ft / 1562 m

Photo:
TIM KEMPLE

FLASHDRY™

DRYING IN MOTION

THE NEW STANDARD IN SWEAT REMOVAL AND TEMPERATURE REGULATION

Better Than Naked™ is engineered with FlashDry,™ our fastest drying fabric ever. Better Than Naked running gear helps regulate body temperature by keeping you cool and dry in variable weather and terrain.

BETTER THAN NAKED™ COLLECTION + FLASHDRY™

thenorthface.com/BetterThanNaked

LONG MAY YOU RUN

If you manage them right, your long runs will help you run better, from 10-Ks to marathons and beyond

> **COMPARED WITH OTHER TRAINING SESSIONS,** the long run is fairly simple—put one foot in front of the other and stop when you've done 20 miles—but its simplicity is deceptive. "The long run is the single most important workout you can do," says coach Jeff Galloway, who ran the 10,000 in the 1972 Olympics, "but it's more complex than you'd think, and most runners don't do it right."

There are many questions about the long run, including the big four: Why? How long? How fast? How often? We'll answer those and also take a look at related issues such as nutrition, rest, and recovery. So put your feet up and read on at a comfortable pace.

WHY DO IT?

Long runs give you endurance—the ability to run farther. Yet they can help 10-K runners as well as marathoners. Long runs do several things:
>They strengthen the heart.
>They open capillaries, speeding energy to working muscles and flushing away waste from tired ones.
>They strengthen leg muscles and ligaments.
>They recruit fast-twitch muscle fibers to assist slow-twitch tasks—such as marathon running.
>They help burn fat as fuel.
>They boost confidence. "If you know you can go that far in training, it gives you the confidence that with the adrenaline of the race, you can do that, too," says Danielle Sanderson, former European 50-K champion.
>They make you faster. "Increase your long run from six miles to 12—change nothing else—and you will improve your 10-K time," says Galloway.

HOW LONG SHOULD YOU GO?

It's not an exact science, but there are two general rules:

TIME IS A BETTER GAUGE THAN DISTANCE

"The duration of the long run will vary depending on the athlete's age, fitness, and the competitive distance they're training for," explains Norman Brook, Britain's former national endurance coach. "The run should usually be for at least 45 minutes and can extend up to three hours for elite athletes and those preparing for the marathon or ultradistance events."

Measure your long runs by all means, if it helps, but for the most part, the goal of a long run is not covering a certain distance, but quality time spent on your feet.

RUN FOR ONE-AND-A-HALF TO TWO HOURS

That's the minimum—roughly 10 to 16 miles—needed to maintain a high endurance level. Increase your long runs by no more than 15 minutes at a time. "Build up to the long run gradually," Brook advises. "If the longest you're running in training is 30 minutes, gradually build up to an hour by adding five minutes to your run each week." A few minutes of extra running makes a difference—but do too much and you're setting yourself up for injury or illness.

HOW FAST?

You want to run a marathon in 3:30, which is eight-minute mile pace, so you do your long runs at that pace. Sounds logical, right? Wrong. "Running isn't always logical," says Benji Durden, a 2:09 marathoner who now coaches both elite and recreational runners. There are reasons for going easy on your 20-milers:

THE LONG ROAD
Increase your distance gradually to avoid burning out.

IMAGE: ALAMY

>Long runs at race pace may be training sessions in your mind, but they're races to your body. That can lead to overtraining, injury, or illness. "Running long runs fast causes more problems than any other mistake," says Galloway. Marian Sutton, winner of many marathons, agrees: "There's no point pushing too hard. Run at a pace that feels comfortable."

>Fast long runs miss the point. "Long runs are for endurance," says Sanderson. "It's amazing how quickly they reduce your resting heart rate, making your heart more efficient."

>The ideal pace for long runs is at least one minute per mile slower than your marathon pace. "The intensity of effort is low, and you should ensure a steady state is maintained," says Brook. "You should be able to conduct a conversation during the run without discomfort."

>You might even walk at points during longer runs—it works for Sanderson. "It's good to just plod round, walk a bit if you need to, or even stop for a break," she advises.

HOW OFTEN?

Don't run long more than once a week. It is, after all, a hard session, requiring rest or easy days before and after. The other end of the scale is debatable. Some runners have no problem going two or three weeks between long runs. Others will come back with a mid-week long run if a shorter race precludes the weekend session.

Galloway recommends a simple formula: roughly one day's gap per mile of your long run. For example, if your long run is 12 to 17 miles, you can go two weeks between long runs without losing endurance; if it's 18 to 23 miles, three weeks. "That is, if you're running at least 30 minutes every other day in between," he adds. This rule can also be used to taper before a marathon. For instance, if your last long run is 22 miles, you'd run it three weeks before race day. If it's 16 miles, you get a two-week rest before the race.

WHICH DAY IS BEST?

Sunday is traditional, because that's when most people have the most free time. Also, most marathons are on weekends, so why not set your body clock in advance? There's no need to stick to a set day. "I'm not rigid about the day I do my long run," says world marathon record holder Paula Radcliffe, "because I never know when I'll be racing." Sanderson also plans her schedule around events. "I do my long run on a Sunday, unless I'm racing," she says.

DON'T GO SOLO

Contrary to popular opinion, long runs aren't boring. You just have to know how to run them—that is, with friends. Find a Saturday or Sunday morning group, or arrange to meet a training partner regularly. "I do some of my runs with friends," says Sanderson, "and the time always goes so much faster."

SPEEDWORK FOR EVERY RUNNER

It may be a cliché, but that's because it's true: The only way to run faster is to run faster

> **MOST OF US CAN COME UP WITH PLENTY OF REASONS TO AVOID SPEEDWORK:** It hurts; it increases our chances of picking up an injury; it makes us too tired for our other runs; we don't need it for running marathons...the list is endless. The thing is, they're all unnecessary fears. What's more, whether you want to beat an ancient 800-meter PR set on the grass track at school, or out-kick the runner who always sprints past you in the local 10-K, adding speedwork to your routine will be immensely rewarding.

Speedwork doesn't just make you run faster. It makes you fitter, increases the range of movement in your joints, makes you more comfortable at all speeds, and will ultimately help you run harder for longer. If you've already added a speed session or two to your schedule, then you'll know all of this already. If you haven't, then here are a few things to remember.

IMAGE: JASON GOULD

EASE INTO IT

When you started running, you ran for just a couple of miles every other day, and gradually built up to your current mileage. You didn't suddenly start running 35 miles a week, so adopt the same approach to speedwork. Put at least three months of steady running behind you, then start with just one session every 10 days or so. Then go on from there.

NOT TOO HARD

Speed sessions aren't about sprinting flat-out until you're sick by the side of the track. They're about controlling hard efforts and spreading your energy evenly over a set distance or time, just like you would in a perfect race.

PACE YOURSELF

When you first start speedwork, you may find monitoring your pace difficult. If you've run a 5-K race, you'll know how that pace feels, but don't panic if you haven't—you'll find the right pace through trial and error. Don't be afraid to make mistakes, but don't worry about being overcautious at first—it's better to build up gradually than fail and hate speedwork.

WARM UP AND COOL DOWN

Before each session, jog for at least eight to 10 minutes to raise your blood temperature, increase blood flow to the muscles, and psych yourself up for the fast running ahead. Follow that with some gentle stretching, and then run a few fast strides before getting down to the tough stuff. Afterward, jog for another five to 10 minutes before stretching again.

FIND A PARTNER

Speedwork takes more effort and willpower than going out for a gentle jog. It's much easier and more fun to train with someone else—and if you really want to improve, try running with someone just a bit quicker than you are.

QUALITY, NOT QUANTITY

Speed training should not account for more than 15 percent of your total mileage. So slot in your speed sessions around the regular work you've been doing all along.

TYPES OF SPEEDWORK

REPETITIONS/INTERVALS Periods of hard running at 5-K pace or faster, between 200 and 1200 meters in length, or 30 seconds and five minutes. Recovery periods can be short (30 to 90 seconds), or of an equal time or distance to the reps. Running at harder than race pace for short periods not only improves speed, but also allows you to work on your running form. When you're pushing hard, it's important to concentrate on things such as arm and hand motion, posture, and stride length. If you can keep these together during a hard session of reps, it will be easier to do so during a race. Don't attempt reps until you've tried other types of speedwork for a couple of months.

TEMPO INTERVALS These are longer than ordinary intervals in that they take between 90 seconds and 10 minutes (or between 400 meters and two miles) and are run a little slower than your 5-K pace. These work a bit like threshold runs— they raise the point at which lactic acid builds up in the muscles.

FARTLEK *Fartlek,* Swedish for "speed play," is the fun side of speedwork and is best done on grass or trails. You simply mix surges of hard running with periods of easy running, with no set structure. Run fast bursts between lampposts or trees when you feel like it, and as hard as you like. Great for newcomers to speedwork.

HILLS Simple: Find a hill that takes between 30 seconds and five minutes to climb at 85 to 90 percent effort, and run up it. Then jog back down to recover. A great alternative to track intervals.

SESSIONS TO BUILD SPEED

These routines will keep your training fresh and make you faster, especially when you want a finishing kick at the end of a race

>> BEGINNERS
IF YOU HAVEN'T TRIED SPEEDWORK BEFORE, HERE ARE SOME (RELATIVELY) GENTLE INTRODUCTORY SESSIONS

1 KEEP IT SHORT
You could start with a session of brisk efforts. Six minutes brisk, one-minute walk, six minutes brisk, one-minute walk, six minutes brisk, and so on.

2 ADD SOME FARTLEK TRAINING
To begin, add some quick bursts into your shorter runs. Each burst can be as little as 20 seconds or as much as a few minutes.

3 DO AN INTERVAL SESSION
6 x 1 minute, with three-minute jog/walk recoveries, or 5 x 2 minutes with five-minute jogs.

4 GO FOR SHORT REPS
After two months or so of speedwork, try your first session of short repetitions: 5 x 300 meters, with four-minute recoveries; 5 x 200, with three-minute rests; or 10 x 200 with three-minute recoveries.

5 GLIDE DOWNHILL
On downslopes during long runs, go with the hill and allow it to pick up your pace to around 80 to 85 percent of flat-out, allowing gravity to power you downhill. Don't go any farther than 150 meters. The idea is to speed up without using any extra energy.

>> INTERMEDIATES
ONCE YOU'VE TRIED A FEW SESSIONS, YOU MAY WANT TO BUILD UP YOUR EFFORTS WITH SOME OF THESE

6 DO A PYRAMID SESSION
So called because you start with a short distance, gradually increase, and then come back down again. For example, start at 120 meters, add 20 to each rep until you reach 200, then come back down to 120. Run these at 400-meter pace, with a walk-back recovery.

7 TRY FAST REPS
For 200 or 300 meters: Run 6 to 10 x 200, with three-minute recoveries, or 5 to 8 x 300, with five-minute recoveries. Start both at 800-meter pace, eventually running the last reps flat-out. You can also combine the two—e.g., 3 x 200, 2 x 300, and 3 x 200.

8 DO A SIMULATION SESSION
This should replicate an 800-meter race. Run two sets of either 500 + 300 or 600 + 200 at your target 800-meter pace, with 60 seconds or less to recover.

9 BUILD YOURSELF UP
Find a large, open area such as a soccer field. Mark out a circuit of roughly 800 to 1000 meters. Once you've warmed up, run a circuit at your 5-K pace, jog for five minutes, then run a second circuit about three seconds faster than the last. Continue speeding up by three seconds until you've completed five circuits.

MAKE STRIDES
These training tips will get
you from A to B faster.

IMAGE: ALAMY

10 KEEP GOING

Now try 5 x 800 meters at a pace 10 seconds faster
per 800 than your usual 5-K pace. Recover between
intervals for the same amount of time it takes you to
run them. As you get fitter, increase the reps.

11 PILE ON THE MILES

Begin with a three-mile warmup, then 4 x 1 mile at a
pace faster than your 10-K pace, with a three-minute
jog between each. Jog to cool down.

12 BUILD YOUR PYRAMIDS...

They work for long distances, too. Try 1000 + 2000 +
3000 + 2000 + 1000 meters at half-marathon race
pace, with a four-minute recovery between each.

13 ...OR DO A HALF PYRAMID

If you're short on time, try 400 + 800 +
1200 + 1600 + 2000 meters, each run faster than your
10-K pace but not flat-out. Jog a 400 between each.

14 CARVE UP A 2-K SPEED SESSION

Divide 2000 meters into: 400 meters at 5-K race pace,
with a 400 jog; 300 at race pace, with a 300 jog; 200
slightly quicker than race pace, with a 200 jog; 100
slightly quicker, but still not flat-out, with a 100 jog.

15 GO LONGER

Run five miles, alternating three-minute bursts at
10-K pace with 90-second recoveries between each.

16 GO OFF-ROAD...

Find a flat stretch of trail or grass and jog for 10
minutes, then run at your mile pace for 1:40; slow
down to a jog (don't walk), and recover for three
minutes, then repeat another 100-second burst. Try
four of these sessions to begin with, and gradually
work up to 10. These 100s work on speed without the
need for a track.

17 ...OR USE A TRACK

At a track, warm up, then run eight laps, alternating
fast and slow 200s. The fast 200s should be hard, but
not a full sprint—you'll soon learn just how fast you
need to go. Add an extra lap as you get fitter.

18 BUILD UP TO 5-K

Run 5 x 1000 meters. Do the first 800 at your 10-K
race pace, then accelerate to 3-K pace for the last 200,
with three-minute recoveries.

19 BREAK UP THE LONGER RUNS

Run at marathon pace for five minutes, then increase
your speed to 10-K pace for one minute. Continue this
sequence until 30 minutes has elapsed.

20 DIVIDE YOUR TIME

Here's a great session for 10-K-plus distances. If you
want to complete a marathon, say, in three hours 27
minutes, then run 800-meter reps in three minutes
and 27 seconds. If you aren't planning a marathon,
run them at 10-mile race pace.

HEIGHTS OF PASSION

It's worth learning to love them—with the right approach, hills can help you become a much better runner

HILLS ARE HARD. That is why many of us run 'round them rather than over them in training. It's not just training, either. It's possible to avoid hills at races if you always choose flat courses. But while running hills might be exhausting and demoralizing if you're not used to them, with the right training and attitude, hills will make you not only faster but a stronger, tougher runner, too, both physically and mentally.

"Hills are a challenge but bring huge rewards for those who regularly include them in their training mix," says Nick Anderson, British cross-country coach and runner. He ensures that all his athletes' training schedules include hills, even when they're racing on the flat. "Hills make you tough and give you confidence," he says. "If you can work for 10 minutes uphill, then working for 10 minutes on the flat will seem easier." And easier running means faster running.

Hills won't just make you faster—they'll make you stronger, too, which is good news if you're a runner who focuses on weekly mileage at the expense of improving muscular strength. "Running hills will make you physically stronger and improve both speed endurance and mechanical efficiency," says Anderson. In other words, if you skip circuit training or weights at the gym, hills will give your body the strength to run faster for longer without breaking down.

GOOD HEALTH

The strength you build when training on hills will also help you run injury-free. Hills, especially when run off-road, provide a great total-body workout that will protect against stresses and strains. "I pick up fewer injuries when I train on hills," says Angela Mudge, who became the Buff Skyrunner World Champion in 2006 after completing a worldwide series of trail races at altitude. "The ever-changing terrain means that each foot placement is subtly different, so you don't tend to develop the repetitive injuries experienced on roads." The ascents will make you a more powerful runner, but the descents are just as helpful: The balance and the need to constantly change stride length when you're coming downhill will make you more agile.

TRY THIS Train off-road as often as possible. The forgiving terrain protects against injury, while uneven surfaces improve your balance and core strength.

SKILL SET

"Off-road hill running suits athletes who can easily change their rhythm," says Mudge. Unlike the track or road, the terrain changes quickly and you need to be able to adapt—from walking up a steep incline to breaking into a run as soon as the gradient levels out. You also need to be good at descending: There's no point becoming powerful enough to hammer up the climbs if you hold back on the descents.

TRY THIS Work on your mental toughness. What might seem like an easy climb at the start of a race will be harder toward the end, but if you're determined, running inclines instead of walking them will make a real difference to your overall race time.

CHECK YOUR PACE

If you find that you start every ascent full of energy and enthusiasm only to fade alarmingly before you're even halfway up, you're setting off too fast. And that, as you will find out to your cost, can spell disaster further into the run. "If your oxygen and energy consumption are too high early on, you'll pay back your oxygen debt later by slowing down and running out of glycogen," says Anderson. You're also likely to experience that burning in your legs (from lactic acid) much sooner.

Forget speed when you start running hills: It's effort that you should focus on. "Aim to keep your effort constant," says Anderson. Try to keep your heart rate at a constant level to preserve energy. You can use a heart-rate monitor to keep track of this. If you're having to put more effort in, it's okay to slow down. You can even walk, but make sure your effort level remains constant.

TRY THIS Hold back a little on the climb. "You'll be able to descend much more quickly because your body will be fresh enough to react to the terrain," says Mudge. There is one exception to the "even effort" rule: "It's okay to hammer the descents in shorter races," says Mudge, "as long as you take them easier if you know there are several ups and downs in longer events."

ON THE UP

You'll develop your own strategies for conquering hills, but borrowing tips from elite runners can help. As well as organizing the Montrail Ultrarunning Championships—a series of 12 mountain and trail races of over 30 miles—Mark Hartell is a former winner of the elite class of the Lowe Alpine Mountain Marathon, and the record holder for the most Lake District peaks climbed during the United Kingdom's 24-hour Bob Graham Round. He always prepares himself for an upcoming hill. "If you know there is a big ascent coming up, slow down a little, try to relax, and prepare yourself mentally to 'float' up the hill," he says. "Running hills is about getting your breathing right, too. It should be quite a meditative process. Try to breathe in time with your footsteps."

TRY THIS Hartell suggests running three strides as you breathe in—making sure you pull air right into your lungs—and three strides as you exhale, forcing the used air out a little more quickly.

OVER THE TOP

When you're near the top of a hill, work your arms hard to maintain rhythm. "Always push for a point just beyond the summit," says Hartell, "and keep your faster breathing pace going for longer to help to expel built-up lactic acid." The oxygen you take in will speed up this process.

TRY THIS Aim to maintain the same strong effort for at least one more minute when you've reached the summit, even if you feel like easing off a little.

ROUTE MAP

Becoming fitter will help you run more quickly on both the ascents and descents, but there are other ways to save time when tackling hills. "Learn to navigate," says Mudge. "You can save time if you follow the best route rather than the runner in front." Start with shorter races where you can practice navigating in a safe environment.

TRY THIS Think about investing in a pair of off-road shoes. These specialized models feature studs on the outsole for extra grip and a lower-slung sole so you're less likely to turn an ankle. Inov-8 and Salomon shoes are popular with hill runners.

THE PERFECT HILL

"The perfect hill to train on is the one nearest to you," says Hartell, "because what matters is that you get out there and do it." Different gradients do suit different types of training, though. Do short repetitions on steep slopes and longer repetitions on gradual gradients. If you only have a short hill to train on, you'll just have to run up and down it more times. In terms of the surface you choose to run on, grass and trails are easiest on the body, but the only hills that aren't suitable to train on at all are ones where you can't get a good grip.

THE SCIENCE OF HILLS

To really understand how hills work to improve running capacity, you need first to understand that the movement of the human body during running is similar to the bouncing of a ball. When a ball hits the ground, its shape changes and it decelerates until the energy is released, and it springs back into shape as it bounces off the ground. Like the human body, the ball flies upward and forward to its next impact with the ground. Athletes can improve their running efficiency by letting the stretch and recoil of muscles do even more of the work needed to "bounce" them forward.

The energy that returns after each footfall is greater when a runner trains on an incline. Studies have shown that, on hills, calf muscles contract more quickly when the foot is on the ground. The calf muscles become more powerful by working at a higher rate.

TRAINING

TRY THIS Find a hill with a gradient of about 10 percent. "That means not too steep and not too shallow," says Anderson. The important thing is that you can maintain good form on the ascent.

TRICKS OF THE TRADE

No matter how hard you train, some hills will always present a mental as well as physical challenge. It can help to break a hilly training run or race into manageable chunks. "If I know a race has seven hills, I never worry about each one until I'm climbing it," says Ian Holmes, four-time British hill-running champion.

You might also be able to push yourself harder if you try to stay with the runner in front. "If I'm struggling, I try to hang on to the group I am with until I get over my bad patch or they leave me for dead," says Mudge. "I think about the next part of the race where I will be able to use my strengths, and try to get there fast."

You can even stop thinking about the hill entirely: "Looking at the left-right, left-right of my feet helps to increase the metronomic effect," says Hartell. Imagining a beat in your head will also help you maintain a steady rhythm.

TRY THIS If you're struggling up a hill, stop thinking about it and focus instead on how much fun you'll have when you reach the top and begin to descend.

NEED FOR SPEED

Some runners use hills as a substitute for speedwork, but Anderson advises against this. True speedwork on flat ground is conducted over distances of less than 50 meters, but hill running can be a good alternative to longer flat intervals. "If you spend time in an endurance phase of training, running lots of miles, putting in threshold runs and hill sessions, you will probably be able to run faster for sustained periods in longer intervals on the flat," says Anderson.

TRY THIS Hills shouldn't replace short repetitions on flat ground, but add them to your schedule if you're currently just focusing on longer interval sessions.

HAVE MORE FUN

If the burning sensation in your lungs and legs leads you to avoid hills, there are ways to make them more tolerable. "I found that running hills became fun when I started passing other people in races. It was that simple," says Hartell. If you're training, run with other people and reward yourself after your effort.

TRY THIS "Pick an area with gorgeous views and enjoy them on the way up," says Mudge.

HILL STARTS

Whether you're training for a 5-K or a marathon, these hill sessions created by Nick Anderson will toughen you up.

THRESHOLD HILLS

Hills run at threshold pace (the speed you can sustain with good form for around 40 minutes) with a downhill recovery run at a similar effort will build endurance and strength. Find a gradual slope that you can run up for 45 seconds to five minutes at 80 to 85 percent of maximum heart rate.

TRY THIS Run one minute uphill followed immediately by one minute downhill. Repeat 12 to 20 times. If you're new to hills, break the session into segments and build up to one continuous block of effort.

BEST FOR The muscular endurance benefits are massive. They really benefit marathon runners who fatigue in the later stages of a race.

SPEED ENDURANCE HILLS

These hills increase power, strength, speed endurance, and mechanical efficiency. They are run at speed (85 to 90 percent of maximum heart rate) with the arms driving and pumping hard and with a long, bounding stride and high knees. These hills are tough and run above threshold, creating high lactate levels.

TRY THIS Complete a session of eight to 12 times 30- to 45-second hills on a good gradient, with a walk or jog back to the start to recover.

BEST FOR Try these if you're a cross-country, 5-K, 10-K, or middle-distance track runner.

OFF-THE-TOP HILLS

You wouldn't run hard up a hill in a race only to start walking when you reach the top, so train by running hard up the hill and continuing at a hard pace once you've reached the summit.

TRY THIS Find a route that has hills that take 30 to 90 seconds to climb, and run these hard each time you hit them. Then run for the same time at the same effort after you reach the top.

BEST FOR Giving you confidence to put some time over your rivals at the top of hills during races.

>> THIS WAY UP
PROPER FORM HELPS YOU POWER UP ANY INCLINE

HEAD
"Keep your head upright and your neck relaxed," says running coach Richard Holt. This will help you maintain a steady breathing pattern. "There's no need to jut it forward to lean into the hill," he says.

EYES
"Keep your eyes focused about 20 feet directly ahead of you," says ex-British hill-running champion Keith Anderson. "This will help keep your head straight—and keep your eyes away from the task ahead."

HANDS
"Keep your hands loose," advises Paula Coates, author of *Running Repairs: A Runner's Guide to Keeping Injury Free*. Loose hands help your whole body stay relaxed.

LEGS
"Push your legs off and up, rather than into, the hill," says Olympian Adam Goucher. This helps you feel as if you're "springing" up the hill.

GOING UP
"If the gradient is constant, keep your pace constant," says Anderson. Otherwise, create a strategy to manage it. "If necessary, adopt a hill-runner's walk," advises Anderson. "Place your hands on your legs above the kneecap and below the quadriceps, and use them to push off."

BRAIN
"You need a 'bring it on' attitude," says Anderson. "You'll need to drive to reach the top. Remember that your training is evidence that you can beat the hill, so go for it."

ARMS
You need to drive those arms to get to the top, but don't overdo it. "Keep the motion of your arms proportionate to the effort the hill requires," says Anderson. Keep your elbows at 90 degrees. "Focus on driving the elbow behind you—it will come forward all on its own," says Holt.

TORSO
"Lean into the hill slightly," says Coates. "This will keep your pelvis in position to drive through the legs and maintain momentum."

FEET
You need to stay on your toes—literally. "Push yourself off from your forefoot using your calves and your quads," says Holt. "The braking action of a heel-strike would be even more exaggerated than it is on the flat, slowing you down significantly."

GOING DOWN
Downhill running is "an art form in itself," says Anderson. Your feet should land beneath you, and a shortened arm swing helps shorten the strides.

ILLUSTRATION: TIN SALAMUNIC

RISE OF THE MACHINE

Looking to broaden your running experience? Spend some quality time with it indoors—on the treadmill

> **IN 1980 BENJI DURDEN HAD A SECRET.** The soon-to-be U.S. Olympic marathoner was sneaking over to the local university physiology lab to work out on (gasp!) a treadmill. "I didn't tell other runners I was using a treadmill," he recalls, reflecting the disparaging attitude toward treadmills at the time. "They would have thought I was strange. Even the lab staff thought I was crazy." They soon revised their thinking when Durden clocked 2:09 and won many marathons in the following years.

Still, it took many years for the idea of treadmills to take hold. At the time, they were considered tinny, cheap, noisy contraptions that cluttered the spare room and did little else (except deliver pangs of regret to their owners). It seemed, like the hula hoop, Rubik's Cube, and mullet hairstyle, doomed to be nothing more than a fad. Few serious runners owned one, and those who did kept it quiet. The distance-running ethic was an outdoors one—no matter the conditions. To run indoors on a rattly machine was...well, a sellout really. Treacherous. Weak.

Fortunately that attitude has changed—as have treadmills, which are vastly superior machines today. Just as cross-training doesn't diminish you as a runner, neither does engaging in a treadmill session. Once you've decided to try treadmill running, you just need to figure out how to incorporate it into your schedule to maximize its potential (and yours). The advantages of treadmills are numerous: from convenience to workout precision to injury prevention.

BEAT THE COLD

It's February and freezing outside, so you step on your treadmill for a six-mile run that sure beats scampering around on icy footpaths. This is the most obvious reason to use a treadmill. Severe winter weather can be tough to train in—as well as potentially dangerous. You may know people who prided themselves on running every winter day, no matter how miserable the weather was—that is, until they hit an ice patch and ended up in a cast for two months and out of running for four. "I don't mind the

INJURY PREVENTION

Ken Sparks, Ph.D., an exercise physiologist at Cleveland State University, recommends treadmill training to come back from injuries—or to avoid them altogether.

>> "First of all, there's less pounding of the joints on a treadmill than on the roads," says Sparks. "The treadmill belt gives when you land on it, unlike concrete and asphalt."

>> "Second, there's no camber on a treadmill as there is on roads. That slope forces you to overpronate (your feet rotate too far inward on impact) and can lead to shinsplints, Achilles tendinitis, and knee problems."

>> "And third, on a treadmill, there's no lateral pressure on your knees and ankles as there would be if you were running around a track, and this kind of pressure can lead to injuries."

NO SLIPUPS
Treadmills help you avoid the risk of falling on ice.

IMAGE: TIMOTHY ARCHIBALD

cold too much," says Bob Kempainen, a 1992 Olympic marathon runner. "But if it's icy, I'll do my 10-mile run on a treadmill. Why risk it?"

BEAT THE HEAT

Severe heat is another reason to head to the gym or wherever there's a treadmill. On a really hot day, an air-conditioned gym may be more attractive than a sticky road surface and punishing sun.

WORK VS. WORKOUTS

Sometimes a quick 30-minute run on the company treadmill at lunch is the only way to fit in a workout between job commitments. Durden, who coaches several runners by phone, remembers a particularly busy month when he and his treadmill became very close. "I did 23 days in a row on a treadmill," he says. "I was afraid that if I went out on a long run I'd miss a lot of calls. It was either that or take a cell phone with me. Cell phones were pretty big back then, so it wasn't really practical."

PRECISION TRAINING

"Treadmills give you a much more evenly paced workout than running on a track," says world-class masters miler Ken Sparks. "For instance, if you're doing 400-meter repeats on a track in 90 seconds, you might run the first 200 in 43 seconds and the second in 47. On a treadmill, you can't do that. Each 200 will be exactly 45 seconds."

PERFECT HILLS

Hill workouts are a special feature of treadmill running that win many over—even those, like Durden, who live in hilly areas. "You can duplicate your hill sessions from week to week almost perfectly," says Durden. "If you want to do a two-percent gradient and a one-percent recovery, you just punch some buttons. It's very precise and very easy to do."

RACECOURSE WORKOUTS

Computerized treadmills come with built-in programs that can take you up and down or increase and decrease the pace during your run. They also let you program your own courses. Extreme marathoner Matt Carpenter is a regular treadmill trainer. Carpenter programs in the exact ascent gradients in upcoming races and sets the pace at slightly faster than the course record. One year, Carpenter won a race but missed the record by 33 seconds on a day

MOST ANYTHING YOU CAN DO OUTSIDE, YOU CAN DO INSIDE.

when rain made the footing slippery. "You can't put mud on a treadmill," he quips.

ESCAPE THE LONELY ROAD

Finally, treadmills come in handy for those who don't appreciate the loneliness of the long-distance runner, or those concerned with the safety of solo running.

>>GETTING YOUR TREADMILL LEGS

Once you've adjusted to treadmill running, you can begin to explore myriad ways to employ it, from speed training to hill sessions to recovery runs. Like a new pair of running shoes, a treadmill needs to be broken in—or, rather, you need to be broken in to the treadmill if you are to derive maximum benefits. "The first few times on a treadmill, start off slower than you think you should," says Benji Durden. "You need to become accustomed to it so you don't feel awkward or as though you're going to fall off."

Take Carol McLatchie and her husband, Jim, for example. They are both avid runners, although Jim has had some treadmill "issues." "Jim has been periodically banned from the McLatchie treadmill," says Carol with a laugh. "He just can't get the hang of it. He keeps falling off it. Once he fell off and was lying half-stunned, pressed against the wall, while the belt was whipping around and thumping on his leg. Finally, he reached over and unplugged it."

Jim is a rare case, however. Most people have no problem on a machine once they adjust to the initial strangeness of a moving surface—it's like learning to ride a bike. Once you get the hang of it, it's easy.

"When I'm on the treadmill, I always have this feeling I'm going faster than on the roads," says Carol McLatchie. "Without visual cues, like scenery going by, I get thrown a bit, and my equilibrium can be slightly off when I step off. It's as if I was out at sea, and now I'm on land again. I have sea legs for a few minutes. But you get used to it pretty quickly."

THE TRICK IS NOT MINDING

The monotony of treadmill training is a big

IMAGE: ALAMY

BEAT BOREDOM
Program hills, intervals, and race-courses for variety.

complaint, and even dedicated treadmill trainers won't argue with you on that point. Instead, they'll tell you how they get around it. World-class marathon runner Ken Martin blasts music while on his treadmill. Durden watches Olympics reruns. McLatchie's treadmill is next to a window that looks out on her garden.

Another option is to schedule your treadmill sessions for peak hours at the gym so you can socialize, or at least have something to look at. (But be aware that most gyms have a time limit on treadmills, usually 20 to 30 minutes.) Avoid clock-watching. "If I look at my watch, time crawls by unbearably slowly on a treadmill," says Carpenter.

There's one perfect way of avoiding monotony on a treadmill. You simply take your cue from Peter O'Toole in *Lawrence of Arabia*, who, after extinguishing a match between his fingers, explained "the trick is not minding." And how do you not mind a treadmill workout? Throw in a little pain.

"I never get bored on my treadmill," says Sparks, who treadmill-trains alongside garden hoses, rakes, and spades in his garage. "I know when I step on my treadmill, I'm going to do an intense speed workout." A positive attitude, as ever, is of crucial importance.

THE GREAT OUTDOORS, INDOORS

With few exceptions, anything you can do outside,

you can do inside. Prior to his 2:09:38 second-place finish at the 1989 New York City Marathon, Ken Martin logged all his long runs on a treadmill. "I'd just get into a nice rhythm and stay controlled," he says. "I also thought it was good because I had my drinks right there beside me, so I didn't have to stop to drink, and I could practice drinking on the run."

But Martin's may be a special case. Many runners can't tolerate a two-hour easy run going nowhere, even if audio-visual entertainment is on hand to ease the pain and/or boredom. Other workouts, such as tempo runs, hills, speedwork, and specially designed racecourse sessions, are more suited to the treadmill because the session is broken up into more easily digestible segments.

MAKING SPEEDWORK COUNT

Sparks has been running intensive speed sessions on a treadmill since the late 1960s, when he was a graduate student under David L. Costill, director of the Human Performance Laboratory at Ball State University near Indianapolis. "I didn't have much time back then, and some of my workouts would actually be jumping on a treadmill and running a four-minute mile, then jumping off," he says.

These days, on his homemade treadmill, Sparks clicks off 63-second 400-meter intervals with a one-minute jog in between. But don't try this at home—or at the gym. Most treadmills won't go faster than a 75-second 400-meter pace. So you might want to limit your speed sessions on a treadmill to longer repeats of, say, 800 meters or miles.

TOP TIPS

>> Treadmill running is precise, convenient, safe, and can reduce injuries.
>> Take the time to accustomize yourself to treadmill running to avoid accidents and injury.
>> Treadmills are blissfully immune to extreme weather.

>> If your employer has a treadmill, employ it for extra lunchtime runs.
>> Make the most of your treadmill's interval and hill settings.
>> Input a race's exact gradient changes and distance to gain an edge.

RUN STRONG

Work out your running muscles to improve performance and injury-proof your body

HOW TO DO THIS CIRCUIT Check with a health-care professional if you're new to exercising. Start with a 10-minute warmup of easy running or cycling. Perform the exercises in order, taking the minimum possible rest between each one. Rest for three minutes before repeating the circuit. Do this session two to three times a week for up to six weeks.

THE PENDULUM

1 Stand on one leg with your shoulder blades drawn back and core braced.
2 Lift one leg straight up behind you while reaching to your toes with the opposite arm. Keep your hips level.
REPS 10 (each leg)
WHY This move works the muscles at the side of your backside to prevent lateral hip movement.

REVERSE LUNGE INTO STEP-UP

1 Step back into a lunge with your right leg until your left thigh is level with the floor.
2 Drive forward, lifting your right leg up onto a step and stepping up. Drive your left leg up and forward before stepping back with it.
REPS 10 (alternate legs)
WHY It trains your leg muscles to be strong, as they lengthen as well as contract.

PLANK TO ONE-ARM ROW

1 In the plank position, hold your body in a straight line from ankle to neck.
2 Take one hand off the floor, and without tilting your torso or moving your core, lift the hand until the elbow goes past your ribs. Hold for two seconds.
REPS 10 (each arm)
WHY Your core will work hard to stabilize your body.

SQUAT TOUCHDOWN

1 Contract your abdominals and take one foot off the floor.
2 Squat by bending at the hip, knee, and ankle, lowering your right hand to the outside of your left foot.
REPS 10 (each side)
WHY Improving neuromuscular stability across your body and overall leg strength will make you a stronger runner.

SINGLE-LEG BRIDGE

1 Lie with your knees bent. Lift your hips to form a line from shoulder to knee, resting your hands on your hips.
2 Lift one foot off the floor, making sure that your hips don't tilt or buckle. Straighten the leg if you can.
REPS 10 (each side)
WHY Poor weight transfer through your pelvis after each footfall can lead to injury.

TOE RAISE

1 Stand with hands on hips and shoulders drawn back.
2 Raise your right toes off the floor while keeping your heel on the ground, and hold for five seconds.
REPS 10 (each side)
WHY Despite the small movement, this exercise is vital for overpronators, and will prevent shinsplints. It will also give you lower-leg strength and stability.

STRETCH IT OUT Follow every workout with a good stretching routine

KNEELING STRETCH

1 Place your right knee on the floor and bend your left leg. Raise your arms.
2 Lean forward to feel the stretch in your hips and side abs. Hold for 30 seconds.
REPS 3 x 30 seconds (each side)
WHY Stretches your hip flexors and core to ease the tension that running causes.

INVERTED V

1 Get onto hands and knees.
2 Take your knees off the floor and press your heels into the floor with your bottom in the air.
REPS 3 x 30 seconds
WHY This stretch was used by female winner in the Cuba Trail Marathon 2007, Kyrin Hall, to loosen up hamstrings, calves, and lower back.

QUADS STRETCH

1 Lie supporting your weight on your left arm, and place a foam roller under your left thigh.
2 Brace your core and glutes and roll forward and backward slowly.
REPS 30–90 seconds (each side)
WHY Stretches the quads without tensing ligaments.

STANDING PIGEON

1 Rest your right leg on a table so it is at 90 degrees to your body.
2 Step back slightly with the supporting leg and relax your upper body over the leg on the table.
REPS 3 x 30 seconds (each side)
WHY Targets the glutes, lower back, and calves.

ILLUSTRATIONS: ANNE CAKEBREAD

PERFECT FORM

Give your gait a makeover to run stronger, longer, and injury-free

> There is actually no such thing as "perfect" form. There, we said it. Runners—like everyone else—come in far too many shapes and sizes to take a one-form-fits-all approach to our sport. However, there are certain elements of form that, if you get them right, can make your technique more efficient. Take these eight examples, and then perform the drills to help you be a better runner.

1 UP YOUR UPPER BODY
Core strength is essential for good posture. An upright posture with a slight forward lean ensures efficient forward acceleration and reduces stress on the body.
Drill: Stand on the balls of your feet, just less than shoulder-width apart, and use your abdominal muscles to control your posture for 60 seconds while keeping your balance.

2 KNEE-SY DOES IT
Increase your knees' range of motion during the swing phase. With your knee more bent, you can move faster with less effort.
Drill: Stand in your push-off position, with your left foot forward and your right foot back. Lift your right heel like you're toeing off. From here perform a high knee lift. Replicate this in your runs for 10 to 15 seconds on each side.

3 DON'T CROSS THE LINE
Beware the crossover gait. If you imagine a line between your legs as you run, you need each foot to land on either side of that line. If they cross it, you'll be landing more on the outside of your foot, adding stress to your muscles and tendons.
Drill: Find a line on a track or football field, and run eight 100-meter reps, keeping your feet on either side of the line.

4 POWER UP YOUR QUADS
The forces experienced as your foot hits the ground can be up to three times your body weight. Strong quads control the flexion and minimize the shock.
Drill: Squats. Keeping your arms at your sides, bend at the hips and knees to lower your body until thighs are parallel to the floor. Hold, then press back up. Perform three sets of 10 reps.

IMAGES: LEVON BISS

5 HAPPY LANDINGS
For optimum efficiency, avoid excessive flexion through your joints as you land. Pronounced flexion of the ankle, knee, and hip reduces the impact shock but decreases your rebound. Minimizing it can keep you on the go, faster.
Drill: Cadence counts. During a run, count the number of right footstrikes achieved in 20 seconds. Aim for 30.

6 GET IN THE SWING
If your arms swing across your chest, this can translate to your legs and upset your form. An equal arm swing will help keep your legs straight.
Drill: Stick two labels on your running top, on the side of your rib cage two inches below your chest. Perform 50-meter warmup sprints, drawing your shoulders back and swinging your upper arms forward and back to touch the labels.

7 GO FORWARD
Focus on pushing forward through your hips with each step. This will utilize your gluteal and hamstring muscles in the push-off and keep your center of gravity consistently rolling forward.
Drill: Tire sprints. Tie a tire behind you, and using the resistance, lean forward and perform six 60-meter sprints, fully extending your legs, with walk-back recoveries.

8 UP AND AWAY
Get the most from your push-off—from the point where your foot is flat on the ground to where your hip, knee, and ankle are fully extended. Improving this will help you achieve a faster flight phase.
Drill: High hops. Perform six 50-meter reps high-hopping on alternate legs with a walk-back recovery. Ensure that your leg is fully extended on takeoff every time.

TRAIL MIX

To build a strong, flexible body and an upbeat mental attitude, just let yourself run wild

> **BEFORE YOU TURN THE PAGE** thinking we're about to con you into some crippling cross-country sprint, stop. Trail running is a good thing—it's all about getting out into nature, for the sheer joy of running in gorgeous woods or mountains, or even hidden corners of your local park.

This is what's been attracting runners to the trails since it became a defined category in the early 1990s—and before. "The term *trail running* was partly driven by marketing—shoe companies had this new off-road gear and needed a story to tell," says Paul Magner from Trailplus, a company that organizes trail runs. "However, people had been running off-road for years, but just not thinking of themselves as trail runners per se. What drove it then, as now, is that if you ask anyone what their favorite run is, it won't be a road route."

At the gentler end of the trail scale, running on soft, even ground is a good way to build miles without the repeated impact of crashing your foot down onto concrete. Don't restrict trail running to the occasional joint-saving long run, though. Give yourself a total-body workout using the toughest trails you can find.

YOUR HEAD-TO-TOE WORKOUT If you're new to off-road running, start with even, manmade trails (such as wood-chip trails) and work on your core strength before you switch to the tough stuff. "If you're a novice, chances are you'll strain more muscles than you condition," says cross-country coach Nick Anderson. "Off-road running will work on your core strength and balance, but you need to build muscles up before you go off-road." Try exercises such as the plank, single-leg squats, and exercises on a BOSU trainer to improve your stability.

STRONG FEET Footwear has a huge impact on your trail experience, but if you can, spend some time on very soft trails so that you can wear lightweight trail shoes. The soft ground makes up for lack of cushioning in the shoes and helps strengthen foot and ankle muscles, making you less injury-prone.

STURDY ANKLES For many nervous novices, the potential for sprained ankles is the number one reason they won't stray off-road. In fact, heading off-road is a good way to *prevent* ankle sprains.

STRONG CALVES AND SHINS Pushing through soft ground works your calves much harder than taking off from a firm surface. Be careful if you're prone to calf or Achilles problems, since soft ground stretches them more. Running downhill on trails also works the muscles down the front of your lower leg, as these provide some of the braking power.

STRONG QUADS, STABLE KNEES Downhill and uneven running works your quads harder as they help stop you from falling forward. Because you'll be changing your foot placement with every strike and running on different gradients, you'll be using all of your quad muscles, whereas road running can overuse the larger, outer quads.

HAMSTRINGS AND GLUTES Running uphill works the muscles at the back of your legs, and soft ground will make the exercise harder. "Bounding" up hills is a good way to toughen up.

CORE STABILITY Strong abs, glutes, and back muscles will help you balance on tricky ground, but a strong core also stops other muscle imbalances from building up in the lower body, which helps prevent injuries.

MENTAL STRENGTH Hitting the trails can be a strength-building exercise for the mind or can give it a good break, depending on the conditions. In winter, it's perfect for giving yourself a bit of a challenge. In warmer months, a run in good weather can be just what you need to stay motivated.

IMAGE: ALAMY

TAKE THE PLUNGE
Running off-road can
help prevent injuries,
rather than cause them.

FUEL'S PARADISE

As with most forms of production, low-quality input equals low-quality output. So if you want to produce good running, be good to yourself and consume foods that favor your best running

> **RUNNERS ARE NOT AVERAGE CITIZENS.** We are different from the sedentary folk for whom dietary recommendations were created. We need more calories and protein. More carbohydrates. We need more nutrients in general. And runners go for foods that never figure into government recommendations—like sports drinks, protein shakes, and energy gels.

That's why we've designed this food plan, aimed specifically at runners, that not only is tasty, but also will help keep you on the move.

GET YOUR TIMING RIGHT

Many runners know exactly what they should eat and when they should eat it. It's the practical application of this theory that messes them up. You are either ravenous when you don't want to be (during training) or not hungry when you should be (immediately after training). The problem is when you are planning your run around a busy work schedule, your brain, leg muscles, and stomach aren't always in sync.

An early-morning run, for example, can leave you feeling fatigued during your workday. A midday training session may become no more than an afterthought if hunger overrides your motivation. And an after-work outing may push back your dinnertime perilously close to bedtime.

If you are looking for ways to get back into sync, read on. The following advice will help coordinate your meals with your training schedule, based on the time of day you run.

>> DAWN PATROLLING

To eat or not to eat? That is the eternal question of those who like to run as the sun is coming up. The answer is, if you can, you should fuel up before your morning run. This performs two functions. First, your muscles receive an energy supply to help you power through the run. Second, your entire body, especially your brain, receives the fuel and nutrients it needs for optimal functioning.

It shouldn't be surprising that studies support this, and that eating before a run boosts endurance compared with fasting for 12 hours. People who eat before working out rate the exercise as being better yet less rigorous compared with noneaters.

That said, not everyone can eat before a morning run. If you're the type of person who sleeps until the minute before you head out the door, you might not be able to fit in a meal. Also, eating too close to your run may ruin it by causing nausea or cramps. On the other hand, if you're a true early bird, you may eat breakfast, read the paper, and clean up before you head out.

Here are a few refueling strategies for both types of morning exercisers:

EARLY RISERS

Choose high-carb foods that are low in fat and moderate in protein. Aim for about 400 to 800 calories, which will fuel your training without making you feel sluggish. Drink about eight ounces of water two hours before your run to offset sweat loss.

BOWLING YOU OVER
High-carb, low-fat foods will fuel your training without making you feel sluggish.

IMAGE: THOMAS MACDONALD

Try one of these 400- to 800-calorie prerun breakfasts:
> Two slices of toast, yogurt, and a piece of fruit
> Cereal with fat-free or low-fat milk and fresh fruit
> A toasted bagel topped with low-fat cheese and tomato slices

LATE SLEEPERS

Most runners fall into this category and don't have time to eat and digest a full meal before they head out the door. If you fall into this camp, experiment to see what you can stomach before you train. But you could start off by trying:
> An eight-ounce glass of sports drink
> An energy gel washed down with water

EVENING MEAL SPECIALISTS

If none of these sits well with you just before a run, then fuel up the night before with a large dinner. As long as you don't plan a long or intense run in the morning, a high-carbohydrate evening meal should power you through your prebreakfast session.

>> ON THE RECOVERY

Whether you're an early or late riser, your body needs calories from carbohydrates, protein, and other nutrients after you have finished running. A recovery meal will help fuel your morning at work, preventing postrun fatigue. Eat within an hour of your training and be sure to include both carbs and protein. Some options include:

> A fruit smoothie made with a tablespoon of protein powder
> Eggs on whole-wheat toast and juice or fresh fruit
> Leftovers from dinner—pasta, soup, chili, or even vegetarian pizza are proven winners

>> THE LUNCHTIME CROWD

People who run during lunch hours sometimes find that hunger gets the better of them. That's because if you ate breakfast at 6 a.m., you've gone six hours without food. By noon, your fuel from breakfast is long gone, and your blood sugar may start to dip. Rather than increasing the size of your breakfast (which may just leave you feeling sluggish), you should bring a light, prerun snack to work.

Eat one to four hours before your run to allow enough time for the food to leave your stomach, and consume 100 to 400 calories, depending upon your body size and how much you had for breakfast. Select foods rich in carbohydrate, low in fat, and moderately high in nutrients. Try these midmorning snacks:

> A breakfast or energy bar with five grams of fat or less
> One slice of whole-wheat toast topped with fruit spread
> A 2.5-ounce serving of dried fruit with a glass of vegetable juice
> One packet of instant oatmeal made with fat-free or low-fat milk

POSTRUN LUNCH

The obvious problem with lunch-hour exercise is that you don't have time for lunch. But you need fluid and food to recover and fuel your brain for the rest of the workday. Packing your own lunch becomes a must—unless you have a workplace cafeteria where you can grab food for desktop dining. A well-rounded packed lunch can be put together in less time than you might think. Try these tips:

> Opt for convenience and shop for items that save time, such as yogurt, raisins, nuts, and energy bars.
> Always add fruit. Toss one or two pieces of fruit into your lunch bag for a reliable source of nutrient-packed carbohydrate.

> Make the most of leftovers. Choose any food from the previous night's dinner that you've already packed in a sealed container ready for transport, reheating, and eating.

>> EVENING EXERTIONS

After a stressful day at the office, there's nothing like a run to burn off tension. The problem is you don't always feel like heading out the door if you're hungry or just exhausted. If you do manage to run, sometimes you return home so ravenous you'll gorge yourself on anything in sight as you make your evening meal. Then you might eat dinner as late as 9 p.m. and end up going to bed with a full stomach. Not so good.

WHAT TO DO?

It's very simple—if you can stick to the following two principles:

> Eat healthy during the day to avoid any intestinal problems that might thwart your training plans. And eat often, and enough that you're adequately

SERVING SENSE

When we recommend eight to 15 daily servings of high-carbohydrate food, you may think you'll have to gorge yourself day after day to get the necessary nutrients. But a serving in each of the food groups isn't as hefty as most people think (or hope). Here are a few examples:

Carbohydrate 3.5 ounces of cooked pasta, beans, couscous, or other grains (about the size of a computer mouse); one slice of bread; one ounce of cereal

Vegetables Seven ounces of raw leafy vegetables (about the size of a baseball)

Fruit One medium piece of fruit (about the size of a tennis ball); eight ounces of juice; three to four ounces of chopped fruit

Calcium 16 ounces of milk; seven ounces of yogurt; two slices of cheese

Protein Seven ounces of soybeans; two to three ounces of fish or lean meat (about the size of a deck of cards); two eggs

Healthy fats One ounce of nuts (about 20 almonds); an eighth of an avocado; two teaspoons of olive oil

fueled for your session to avoid the "I'm too hungry" excuse.

> Eat lightly after exercise to recover well without causing digestion that could interfere with your sleep.

BETTER LATE THAN NEVER

Evening exercisers may also want to keep the following in mind:

> Never skip breakfast. Try to eat at least 500 calories for your morning meal. For example, throw together a fruit smoothie made with yogurt, fruit, and juice while you are preparing your toast. Or try cereal topped with nuts, fat-free milk, and a piece of fruit.

> Make lunch your main meal of the day. Focus on high-quality protein, such as fish, tofu, lean beef or lamb, chicken, or bread with cooked grain, along with fresh fruit. A smoothie, juice, and natural yogurt drink are also great, healthy lunch foods.

> Always eat a mid-afternoon snack. Around three hours before your run, have some fruit or an energy bar together with eight ounces of water.

> Drink more fluids. Grab a drink as soon as you step back through the door after your run. And keep drinking as you prepare your meal. This helps replace sweat loss and may prevent you from trying to eat the contents of your kitchen cupboards all at once.

> Eat moderately at dinner. Some people worry about eating too close to bedtime because they fear the calories will go straight to their fat cells. That's simply not true. Your body will use those calories to stockpile fuel in your muscles. On the other hand, if you eat more calories than your body needs—no matter what time of day or night—your body will store the excess as fat.

HEALTHY SNACKS

If your runs last longer than an hour, you can use energy bars, gels, or sports drinks and other performance foods to boost your energy levels. Because these foods contain easily digestible carbs, they make great prerun and postrun snacks, too. Consume about one to two ounces of carbs during each hour of running (most bars contain an ounce or more of carbs; most gels contain about one ounce). Foods such as jelly beans, Fig Newtons, dried fruit, and honey also supply fast, digestible carbohydrate.

IMAGE: JON WHITAKER, MELODY DEAS

BERRY GOOD
Fruit smoothies are a quick and easy breakfast.

TOP TIPS

>> If you run in the morning, try to eat at least an hour before you begin. If you don't have time to prepare and eat food, experiment with sports drinks and energy gels. Or eat a large meal the night before.

>> If you run at lunch, have a mid-morning snack and pack your own lunch to eat afterward at your desk. Always eat fruit.

>> If you run in the evening, eat well during the day to prevent postwork sluggishness. Make lunch the main meal of your day, and eat healthy morning and afternoon snacks.

>> Eating junk food occasionally is not the end of the world. If it's not out of control, don't beat yourself up. Enjoy the treat.

TO YOUR HEALTH

We all know it's important to stay well-hydrated, but few of us are aware that we can have too much of this particular good thing

> **AS HE PASSED HIS FAMILY** on Tower Bridge during the 2007 London Marathon, 22-year-old David Rogers did a star jump. "He saw us and waved, and then leapt in the air," said his father, Chris. "He was doing what he wanted to do."

Tragically, just hours after completing the race, David died in a London hospital, having collapsed once he'd crossed the finish line. The cause? Hyponatremia, following kidney failure due to sodium deficiency, which is caused by excess fluid consumption.

We live in a water-obsessed society. Water bottles have replaced orange slices as the players' refreshment during and after football and soccer games; water coolers are as pervasive as tea bags in office kitchens, and schools increasingly encourage you to send your child to school with their own drink bottle. Why? At least in part because every fitness article in every newspaper and magazine insists that you absolutely, positively must drink eight big glasses, or two quarts, of water per day.

But where's the proof? Amazingly, there isn't any. Even in marathons, the available evidence indicates that overhydrating is as potentially dangerous as underhydrating, with the story of David Rogers serving as an unfortunate exclamation mark. Yes, we runners need to drink generously—no one questions that—but we need to drink with a fuller understanding of the facts, the medical science, and the potential risks.

WATER, WATER EVERYWHERE

Water is by far the largest constituent of the human body, making up about 60 percent of total body weight. This large pool of water performs many crucial functions, including nourishing the cells, carrying food throughout the body, eliminating waste, regulating body temperature, cushioning and lubricating the joints, and maintaining blood volume and blood pressure. Inadequate levels of fluid consumption have been associated with kidney stones and higher rates of urinary tract infections, bladder and colorectal cancers, and even heart disease.

Given this information, all experts agree that an adequate water supply is crucial to the body's optimal functioning. But how much is "adequate"?

THE TWO-QUART MYTH

Most adults—at least those who read the health sections of newspapers or magazines—have come to believe they should drink two quarts of water a day, but there's little to no evidence supporting this rule.

Heinz Valtin, the professor emeritus of physiology at Dartmouth Medical School, committed himself to searching out medical-scientific verification for this theory. He couldn't locate any. "I have found no scientific proof that we must drink two quarts of water a day," concluded Valtin. "The published data strongly suggest that we probably are drinking enough, and possibly even more than enough."

Ron Maughan, visiting external professor of Loughborough University and the foremost researcher on hydration in the United Kingdom, agrees. "You hear this advice from magazines, but where is it actually coming from? Not the Department of Health."

Tim Lawson, director of Science In Sport, a sports nutrition company, believes the two-quart rule might

IMAGE: THOMAS MACDONALD

MAKE A SPLASH
Staying hydrated is
essential for runners.
But don't overdo it.

only apply if "you were eating dehydrated food." He says the figure is misquoted because it fails to take into account the moisture content from food (especially fruit and vegetables) and the fluid intake from other drinks.

Of course, Valtin was researching the hydration habits of nonexercising people. Runners sweat heavily and need to drink more than nonexercisers, and the heavier and more muscular you are, the hotter the weather, and the faster you run, the more you sweat.

THE TRUTH ABOUT CAFFEINE

Meanwhile, a survey of 2,818 adults by the International Bottled Water Association (IBWA) revealed an average adult drinks 4.5 quarts of fluid a day. The IBWA argues that 1.5 quarts of this amount is alcohol and caffeinated drinks (both considered diuretics, meaning that they increase urine production), and should be subtracted from the total.

However, subsequent research has reversed the age-old wisdom that caffeinated beverages are diuretics. Actually, to be more precise, the research confirmed that caffeinated beverages are diuretics but only to the same degree as plain water. If you drink a lot of water, you need to go to the toilet. It's the same with caffeinated beverages—no more, no less.

"Research indicates caffeine stimulates a mild diuresis similar to water," says hydration expert Larry Armstrong. Maughan also reviewed the literature to find that a diuretic effect occurred only when caffeine doses of more than 300 mg were given to subjects whose caffeine intake had been restricted for a few days prior to the test. He also noted the same myths surround alcohol—especially beer—which isn't, he claims, that much of a diuretic.

BEATING A PATH TO THE BATHROOM

If anything, truth be told, we're overhydrated. This isn't necessarily a bad thing. It's probably just adding to your daily mileage and calorie burn, with all those trips to the bathroom, but there's little evidence for dehydration ills—fatigue, headache, dry skin, lack of concentration, and so on—mentioned by some folks.

"Without any convincing data, I remain skeptical of all these so-called dehydration problems," says researcher Barbara Rolls, author of *Thirst,* and a leading expert on hydration. "It's a myth that's being perpetuated. The thirst mechanism is exquisitely tuned to keep us in fluid balance."

Maughan confirms the view that thirst is a useful

mechanism, maintaining that it is simply a learned behavior. Unlike children, who demand a drink as soon as they feel like it but then only have a sip and are unable to finish the drink, adults learn to restrain the immediate impulse to drink.

A MATTER OF SEX

When it comes to sweat rates and fluid-replacement needs, men and women come from different planets. Because men are, on average, significantly heavier than women and have more muscle mass, they sweat more than women and need to drink more.

Women, meanwhile, have a smaller blood-plasma "tank" than men, which is easier to overfill. Many women who are new to marathons are happy to finish in five hours or more. They reach the 20-mile mark exhausted, and think, "If I can force myself to drink more, I'll feel better," even though this is not necessarily the best course of action.

For all of these reasons, a woman's hydration need can be up to 30 percent lower than a man's.

DRINK APPROPRIATELY
Know your body's hydration needs and make adjustments according to the weather.

IMAGE: ALAMY

MODEST DEHYDRATION IS A NORMAL AND TEMPORARY CONDITION FOR MANY MARATHON RUNNERS. EXTREME FLUID CONSUMPTION, ON THE OTHER HAND, CAN BE DEADLY.

when runners were advised to avoid water-drinking because it caused stomach cramps. At any rate, race organizers provided no fluids on the course. The result was that the runners lost five to six percent of their body weight through sweating, but apparently suffered no particular ill effects.

A FULL TANK

Since then, research has shown that anything more than a two percent dehydration will worsen performance, and experts agree that it makes sense to limit dehydration as you run. Some runners can even train themselves to drink more. Studies have also shown that the more fluid there is in your stomach, the more will reach your blood, where you want it. Hence the good advice to run with a comfortably full stomach and to "top off your tank" frequently.

OUT OF THE LAB, ONTO THE ROAD

Nonetheless, in the real world, most runners who finish a marathon in three to four hours will sweat about twice as much per hour as they can drink. This can easily lead to greater than two percent dehydration. Why this scenario? Because the body doesn't like to run hard and drink hard at the same

This essential fact has been largely overlooked and is particularly important for female runners, because most of the marathoners who suffer from hyponatremia, including a number who have died from marathon-related hyponatremia, have been women.

HYDRATION, PERFORMANCE, AND RISK

Dehydration diminishes performance because it thickens the blood, decreases the heart's efficiency, increases heart rate, and raises body temperature, but a modest dehydration is a normal and temporary condition for many marathon runners, and doesn't lead to any serious medical conditions. Extreme fluid consumption, on the other hand, can be deadly.

THE LONG AND SWEATY ROAD

The first dehydration studies with marathoners were done at the Boston Marathon in the 1960s, an era

time. At about a 4:00 pace, it seems, runners are going slow enough, perhaps with walking breaks, to drink sufficiently to avoid most dehydration.

With regard to the often-quoted warnings to avoid greater than two percent dehydration, Maughan emphasizes that "there is no sudden cutoff point—dehydration depends on performance and the individual." He does, however, acknowledge that even one percent dehydration is enough to have a negative effect on performance.

THE SWEAT-RATE PARADOX

As we get fitter, we sweat more. This means we dehydrate faster—a cruel blow, it would seem. In any given marathon, in fact, the winners are probably the most dehydrated runners on the course. At pace, they produce tremendous amounts of heat and sweat, and have no time for drinking. Of course, the body is clever: It knows it can cope with modest dehydration.

Heatstroke is the serious danger. So the body increases your sweat rate as you get fitter, because sweat promotes cooling, which helps keep heatstroke at bay. Dehydration can certainly contribute to heatstroke (which is one of the prime reasons why all athletes are admonished to drink regularly), but it doesn't cause it.

RISE OF HYPONATREMIA

As marathon running has boomed, and particularly as it has attracted more women and recreational runners, hyponatremia has intruded on our sport. It means "low blood sodium," but it's caused by excessive fluid consumption, which lowers the concentration of sodium in the blood. As we've seen, in extreme cases, hyponatremia can lead to brain seizures and death. Maughan describes the condition as "a significant danger for a small number of people."

In 2002, the Boston Marathon and the Marine Corps Marathon had their first-ever fatalities attributed to hyponatremia. Hyponatremia is also beginning to appear in other endurance athletes, including ultramarathoners, Ironman triathletes, and long-distance walkers.

WATER RATES

The hyponatremia issue has forced sports and medical groups to take a new look at their hydration guidelines, and several have already adjusted their recommendations. Recently, the International Marathon Medical Directors Association (IMMDA)

WATER IN, WATER OUT

Your daily water supply comes from three sources, and you lose water in four ways. The percentages shown here are averages for nonexercisers. Runners sweat more, and need to drink more, than nonexercisers. Actual percentages will vary considerably, depending on the weather, your diet, the amount you exercise, and other factors.

WATER INTAKE	%	WATER LOSS	%
Fluids	60%	Urine	50%
Food	30%	Sweat	35%
Metabolism	10%	Respiration	10%
		Feces	5%

Approximately 10 percent of your daily water supply comes from metabolic water—fluid that's "liberated" within the body when you burn fat and carbohydrates.

issued the first fluid-consumption guidelines from a medical organization that was completely focused on and tailored to runners.

IMMDA, which represents some 150 major marathons on all seven continents, suggests that marathoners should consume 13 to 27 ounces of fluid per hour (you'll need more the hotter it is, the harder you run, and the more you weigh), with an absolute ceiling at 27. See www.aims-association.org/immda. htm.

That's just over half the fluid requirement proposed since 1996 by the widely quoted "Exercise and Fluid Replacement" stance of the American College of Sports Medicine, which calls for 20 to 40 ounces per hour. Clearly the scientific jury is still out when it comes to appropriate water consumption.

The Boston Marathon now provides all 20,000 runners with a fold-out pamphlet from the American Running Association and the American Medical Athletic Association. It advises runners to stay hydrated but not to overdrink, to maintain a salty diet, to favor sports drinks, and to recognize warning signs.

The Gatorade Sports Science Institute has recently published one of the most comprehensive advisories on hyponatremia, *Hyponatremia in Athletes*. It

DON'T OVERDO IT
All runners need water,
but women need 30
percent less than men.

reinforces the idea that hydration is important, and that each of us sweats at a different rate, produces varying amounts of sodium in our sweat, and reacts differently to heat stress.

WATER FORESIGHT

We also believe it's a good time to review your hydration practices. Runners need to pay more attention to their daily fluid consumption than most people, but we don't need to be obsessive. Given half a chance, the body will self-regulate to a normal, healthy state of fluid balance.

If you drink a lot of water and get a little overhydrated during the day, that's okay. Your body will simply send you to the bathroom. Conversely, if you can't drink quite enough during a marathon, that's also okay. Sit down with a sandwich and sports drink after the race, and your body will soon soak up the water it needs. Don't rush, and don't over-drink. After a race, you've got plenty of time to rehydrate.

HYDRO THERAPY

Keep the following in mind, and water consumption should never become an issue for you:

DRINK GENEROUSLY, BUT APPROPRIATELY
Know yourself and your needs, and make adjustments for the weather. A runner training while away on vacation in Greece may need to drink more during and after a slow 10-mile run in August than during or after an all-out marathon effort on a cool spring morning. Listen to your body.

USE SPORTS DRINKS Before, during, and after training and races, drink sports drinks made with electrolytes. These contain the water you need, appropriate amounts of carbohydrates, and small amounts of sodium, all of which are essential.

PAY PARTICULAR ATTENTION TO POSTEXERCISE REHYDRATION You're likely to become dehydrated during a long, hard run, so make sure you drink enough afterward. The same goes for food. Drink your fluids, take in your carbohydrates, take in a little sodium, and eat a little protein.

WEIGH YOURSELF DAILY DURING PERIODS OF INTENSE TRAINING If you're losing weight, make sure it's from fat loss, not from chronic dehydration. Maughan's recommendation is to restrict actual weight loss to one percent of body mass. You can also check your urine color. It should be clear or light yellow (unless you have recently taken some B vitamins, which can turn the urine bright yellow).

WHEN RUNNING LONG AND SLOW—THREE OR FOUR HOURS OR MORE—MONITOR YOUR FLUID CONSUMPTION Be sure you're not drinking more than you need. Also, consider running with a salty snack that you consume at the 20-mile mark. If you're a woman, pay particular attention to these recommendations.

DRINK WHEN YOU'RE THIRSTY While it's true that your thirst doesn't kick in until you're one- to two-percent dehydrated, there's nothing wrong with that. Remember that your body has an "exquisitely tuned" water-balance mechanism. Use it.

IMAGE: ALAMY

RUNNER'S WORLD

REAL GOOD EATS

★ ★ ★ ★ ★

A HEALTHY, WHOLE-FOODS EATING PLAN IN SIX COURSES

1 Colorful fruits and vegetables

2 Meat and Poultry

3 Cold-water Seafood

4 Foods with Skins

5 Seeds, nuts and grains

6 Dairy Foods

> **PUT DOWN, FOR A MOMENT,** your energy bars, nutrient-enhanced drinks, and other fortified foods. When it comes to fuel, "real" foods such as fruits, vegetables, whole grains, and lean meats are a far better option. Within the body, vitamins, minerals, and other essential nutrients work together with thousands of other compounds, such as color pigments in fruits and vegetables, special starches and fibers in whole grains, and unique fats in seeds, nuts, and dairy. And it's the whole package, working together, that promotes good health and peak athletic performance. Getting the 50-plus nutrients every runner needs daily, from real food, is easy. Follow these six rules every day, and your body will get everything it needs for better health and better running.

ILLUSTRATIONS: CHARLIE LAYTON; IMAGES: JOSEPH DE LEO

1) EAT FIVE DIFFERENT-COLORED FRUITS AND VEGETABLES DAILY

A plethora of pigments lights up the fruit and vegetable aisle, each offering health benefits. The red in tomatoes comes from lycopene, while orange in sweet potatoes comes from beta-carotene. These and other pigments lower the risk of cancer and heart disease. And since most pigments act as antioxidants, they can help reduce inflammation caused by heavy exercise. For maximum benefit, these pigments need to interact with different color compounds in other fruits or vegetables.

PLATE IT Aim for nine daily servings of colorful fruit and veggies. Of these, try to eat five colors. A serving equals a medium-sized fruit such as an apple; 1/3 cup of dried fruit; one cup of raw veggies; 1/2 cup of cooked veggies; or two cups of green salad.

BASQUE GRILLED VEGETABLE SKEWERS WITH LIME CHIMICHURRI SAUCE

An energizing lunch that will power you through an afternoon workout

YOU WILL NEED
(Makes 8 skewers, serves 4)
3 peppers (green, yellow, red), sliced
2 portobello mushrooms, quartered
2 zucchini, sliced and halved
1 red onion, cut into 2-inch chunks

For the vegetable rub:
Salt and freshly ground black pepper
1/2 Tbsp. chili powder
1 Tbsp. dried orange rind

For the basque-style green sauce:
6 garlic cloves, chopped
3 dried bay leaves
3 limes or 2 Tbsp. key-lime juice
1 green and 1 red chile pepper
1/3 cup fresh flat-leaf parsley, chopped
1/4 cup fresh oregano, chopped
1/2 cup fresh basil, chopped
1/3 cup olive oil

HOW TO MAKE IT
Cover the vegetables with the rub and let them rest. Preheat grill. Make the green sauce with a pestle and mortar or in a blender until a smooth paste. Transfer to a bowl.
Add herbs and juice the limes. Whisk in oil in and set aside. Skewer vegetables and grill. Serve on steamed brown rice and drizzle sauce over. **Per serving:** Calories: 220; Fat: 11g; Carbs: 29g; Protein: 7g

NUTRITION

2) EAT MEAT, POULTRY, OR EGGS FROM FREE-RANGE OR GRASS-FED ANIMALS

By eating lean meats, poultry, and eggs, along with dairy products, runners can easily meet their increased protein needs and take in minerals that can be hard to get elsewhere. Meats are a great source of iron and zinc, which support healthy red blood cells and a strong immune system. Studies suggest that diets balanced with fruits, vegetables, whole grains, and lean meat, including beef and skinless poultry, help lower blood-cholesterol levels, blood pressure, and the risk of heart disease.

PLATE IT Aim for five to seven ounces of lean meat, or the equivalent (1 egg = 1 ounce of meat, protein-wise) a day. Having three ounces of meat supplies 20 to 25 g of protein (25 to 30 percent of your daily need). Trim away fat, and grill or bake rather than fry.

KOTA KAPAMA

A post-long-run cinnamon chicken dinner to refuel and repair working muscles

YOU WILL NEED
(Serves 4)
1 chicken (2 1/2–3 lbs.) cut into eighths
1 tsp. ground cinnamon
2 tsp. salt
1 tsp. freshly ground black pepper
5 peeled garlic cloves, crushed
1 1/2 Tbsp. extra-virgin olive oil
2 peeled, chopped medium yellow onions
1/2 cup dry white wine
1 cup water
1 cup chicken stock
6-ounce can of tomato purée
1 Tbsp. fresh oregano, chopped

HOW TO MAKE IT
Boil water with some salt and set aside. Mix the cinnamon, salt, and pepper in a small bowl. Rub over the chicken.

Heat oil in a large, deep pan over high heat. Add the chicken and brown for 4 to 5 minutes on each side. Remove from heat.

Fry onions and 3 garlic cloves over medium-high heat. Cook until the onions are golden brown. Add wine. When that has evaporated, add water, chicken stock, purée, oregano, and remaining garlic. Add chicken.

Cover and simmer over low heat for an hour or until chicken is tender. Serve over a bed of quinoa or couscous.
Per serving: Calories: 360; Fat: 11g; Carbs: 18g; Protein: 40g

3) EAT FOODS THAT COME FROM COLD WATER

Fish and other seafood provide a unique combination of nutrients important to runners. Seafood is an excellent source of protein (runners need about 50 percent more protein than nonrunners) and also contains zinc, copper, and chromium—minerals that are often low in a runner's diet. But the omega-3 fats are what really count, as they lower the risk of heart attack, vascular disease, and stroke. The fats in fish have anti-inflammatory capabilities, so they can counter muscle soreness.

PLATE IT Eat one or two seafood dishes a week. Fish from colder waters, such as near Alaska, have the greatest amount of omega-3 fats. Swordfish, shark, and king mackerel are the most contaminated fish, so go for salmon, shrimp, and scallops.

SALMON LETTUCE PARCELS

A protein-packed recovery meal that's light on the stomach

YOU WILL NEED
(Serves 4)
4 4-ounce salmon fillets
2 Tbsp. olive oil, plus more to brush fish
Juice of two limes
1 Tbsp. chili powder
1 Tbsp. cumin
1 tsp. cayenne pepper
1 head butter lettuce
1 head radicchio
1 tomato, diced
1 onion, diced
1/2 cup prepared tzatziki
1/4 cup chopped scallions

HOW TO MAKE IT
Preheat grill to the high setting. In a baking dish, combine oil, lime juice, and spices. Add fillets and turn them so every side is coated. Marinate for 10 minutes.

Form the parcels by gently separating the heads of butter lettuce and radicchio. Line a whole leaf of round lettuce with radicchio for each serving.

Brush fillets with oil. Grill until they begin to turn opaque on top. Fish should be firm to the touch, flaking easily.

Flake fish into each parcel. Top with tomato and onion. Drizzle with tzatziki, then garnish with scallions.
Per serving: Calories: 350; Fat: 22g; Carbs: 9g; Protein: 31g

4) EAT PLANT FOODS WITH THEIR SKINS INTACT

Lose the peeler. The outer skins of plants protect them from UV light, parasites, and other invaders. As a result, those skins are bursting with a wide range of phytochemicals that also protect your health. Grape skins, for example, are high in resveratrol, and onion skins contain quercetin, both of which can help lower your risk of heart disease and colon and prostate cancer, and boost your immunity. Skins are also rich in resistant starches and various types of fiber, which promote the growth of healthy bacteria in the intestines and help keep body fat low.

PLATE IT The less you fuss with fruits and vegetables, the better. Wash them, but leave peels and skins on. If using high heat, wrap them in foil to protect their skins.

CURRIED LENTILS WITH BUTTERNUT SQUASH

A satisfying night-before-the-race dinner that won't slow you down

YOU WILL NEED
(Serves 2 as a main dish, or 4 as a side dish)
1 cup dry lentils
1 butternut squash
1 Tbsp. olive oil
1 Tbsp. curry powder
1 tsp. ground ginger
1 tsp. chili powder

HOW TO MAKE IT
Spray a baking dish with cooking spray and set aside. Pour lentils into a deep pot and cover with cold water. Bring water to boil, reduce heat, and add raw chunks of the squash (leave the skin on, remember). Simmer for one hour (or until squash is soft).

After an hour, remove from heat, drain, and set aside. With tongs, pull out the chunks of squash and mash them a bit.

Preheat the oven to 400°F. In a large bowl, mix the lentils and mashed squash with the olive oil and the spices (including salt and pepper to taste). Spoon the mixture into the baking dish.

Bake for around 20 minutes, until piping hot. Serve warm with spinach or cabbage; garnish with shredded coconut if desired.
Per serving: Calories: 530; Fat: 8g; Carbs: 94g; Protein: 32g

5) EAT SEEDS, OR FOODS MADE FROM SEEDS

Seeds, many beans, and even tree nuts (such as cashews, almonds, pecans, and walnuts) contain the mix of nutrients necessary to grow a new plant, which means they are packed with health-boosting compounds. In addition to protein and essential fats, seeds contain bioactive compounds, which act as antioxidants. Eating a diet rich in seeds can improve health and help maintain healthy body weight. They also lower the risk of type 2 diabetes and certain cancers.

PLATE IT Eat four or five servings of whole grains daily (equal to 1/2 cup of brown rice or one slice of 100 percent whole-grain bread), a 1/2-cup serving of beans most days of the week, and a one-ounce serving of nuts or seeds five days a week.

WALNUT AND BLUEBERRY BRAN PANCAKES

A prerun breakfast to top off your fuel tank

YOU WILL NEED
(Makes 8 pancakes, serves 4)
1 1/2 cups whole milk
1 cup instant oats
3/4 cup sifted all-purpose flour (or a blend of white and whole-wheat flours)
1/4 cup oat flour or oat bran
3/4 cup blueberries
1/2 cup chopped walnuts
Tbsp. baking powder
1 tsp. salt
2 Tbsp. honey
2 eggs, beaten

HOW TO MAKE IT
Sift together the flour, baking powder, and salt. Then pour milk over the oats and lightly stir in the eggs.

Add the mixture of dry ingredients, and the honey, to the oats mixture, stirring until combined. When the batter is thoroughly mixed, stir in the blueberries and walnuts. Ladle batches of the batter onto a preheated greased or nonstick frying pan and cook until tops are bubbly and edges look cooked. Turn over and finish cooking the other side.

Per serving: Calories: 400; Fat: 16g; Carbs: 52g; Protein: 15g

NUTRITION

6) DRINK MILK AND EAT MILK PRODUCTS THAT COME FROM ANIMALS

Mammal milk (as opposed to soy milk) and other dairy products, such as cheese and yogurt, should be a part of every runner's diet. Milk supplies calcium for strong bones, and animal milk provides whey protein to speed recovery and boost the immune system, as well as lower your blood pressure and your risk of heart disease. Studies have also shown that dieters who include dairy products lose more fat than those who simply cut calories. Fermented dairy products, such as yogurt and cream cheese, contain live bacteria, which also bolster immune health.
PLATE IT Include two or three servings of low-fat dairy each day (eight ounces of milk, a yogurt, or 1.5 ounces of cheese), with one being a fermented milk product.

SEASONAL-FRUIT SMOOTHIE

An anytime snack that boosts energy and recovery

YOU WILL NEED
(Makes 2 servings)
1/2 cup seasonal fruit (peaches, berries, mangoes)
3/4 cup low-fat yogurt
1 cup milk or soy milk
6 almonds
1 Tbsp. honey (optional)

HOW TO MAKE IT
Peel the fruit, if appropriate, and cut into small pieces. Put all the ingredients into a blender and purée until smooth. Pour into a chilled glass and serve with a straw. You may want to add ice or use frozen fruit if you want to serve it really cold.
Per serving; Calories: 170; Fat: 6g; Carbs: 19g; Protein: 12g

GET REAL A three-day whole-foods eating plan

DAY 1
BREAKFAST
Bowl of oatmeal (1 1/2 cups dry oats),
1 oz. almonds,
1 cup plain yogurt with kiwi and strawberries
LUNCH
Burrito with 1 cup black beans, 1 oz. shredded cheese, 1/2 cup diced tomatoes, 2 Tbsp. diced olives, lettuce, and salsa, on whole-grain tortilla
1/2 cup raisins
SNACK
1 pear, 8 oz. low-fat milk
DINNER
4 oz. baked salmon topped with fresh herbs
4 or 5 small red potatoes, steamed
2 cups of mixed green salad with 2 Tbsp. olive-oil vinaigrette
1 cup mashed butternut squash

DAY 2
BREAKFAST
2 eggs, scrambled
1 whole-grain English muffin spread with 2 Tbsp. soft goat cheese
1 banana, 1/2 cup melon
LUNCH
1 cup low-fat cottage cheese topped with 1/2 cup cherry tomatoes, 1/2 cup diced cucumber, and
1/4 cup toasted wheat germ
4 whole-grain rye crackers
1 oatmeal cookie
1 green apple
SNACK
1 cup plain low-fat yogurt blended with 1 cup frozen mixed berries and 2 Tbsp. honey
DINNER
Stir-fry: 4 oz. top sirloin cut in thin strips, 1 Tbsp. peanut oil, 2 cups frozen stir-fry veggies, and 2 Tbsp. cashews; serve on
1 1/2 cups brown rice

DAY 3
BREAKFAST
2 Tbsp. peanut butter on
2 slices of whole-grain oatmeal bread or toast
1 cup yogurt topped with 1 chopped apple and 4 dried apricot halves
LUNCH
1 1/2 cups lentil soup
2 slices of a whole-grain toast, drizzled with 2 Tbsp. honey
Big handful of raw snap peas and carrot sticks
1 cup low-fat milk
SNACK
1/3 cup trail mix
1 cup pomegranate juice
DINNER
1 chicken leg and thigh baked with 2 Tbsp. pesto
1 cup cooked bulgur pilaf (with onions, garlic, and parsley)
1 cup steamed cauliflower
1 plum and 1/2 cup dates

DAILY NUTRIENT TOTALS:
2,300 CALORIES; 110G PROTEIN; 330G CARBOHYDRATES; 40G FIBER; 70G FAT

BETTER TOGETHER

Mix and match different foods to get more nutrients from every bite

> RUNNERS KNOW that fruits, vegetables, and whole grains are good for us because they contain nutrients that fuel our runs and repair our muscles. But many of us might not realize that while each of these foods is individually nutritious, when they're paired with a complementary counterpart, they can provide more bang with every bite.

"Nature put nutrients in foods to act in synergy with each other," says nutritionist Lisa Blair. "When certain foods are eaten at the same time, their nutrients can work together in a way that provides unexpected health benefits." The following duos are perfect examples of how two can most definitely be better than one.

BAKED POTATO + SPINACH

WHAT IT DOES Boosts iron absorption
FOOD SCIENCE Iron is responsible for transporting oxygen in the blood. Low iron levels can lead to anemia, resulting in fatigue, weakness, and dizziness. The body absorbs as little as two percent of iron from plant foods, compared with up to 25 percent from meat sources. However, says Blair, if we know how to put them together, in the right combinations, we can enhance the overall nutrient value.
PUT IT TOGETHER Have a baked potato and baby spinach salad with dinner. Or stir-fry red and green peppers (a handful provides double your daily need of vitamin C) with tofu, edamame, and kale—all good sources of iron.

RED PEPPER + FETA CHEESE

WHAT IT DOES Cuts heart-disease risk
FOOD SCIENCE Colorful vegetables (red peppers, tomatoes, carrots) are rich in carotenoids, pigments that reduce risk of heart disease. Add some fat, and your veggies get even better, says Steven Schwartz, professor of food science at Ohio State University. "Fat helps carotenoids become more soluble so they can be better absorbed in the intestine and into the bloodstream," he says. Schwartz found that people who ate a salad with avocado absorbed five times more carotenoids than eating it with nonfat dressing.
PUT IT TOGETHER Top your salad with feta cheese, avocado, or salad dressing. Or sauté vegetables in olive oil or butter.

ROSEMARY + BEEF

WHAT IT DOES Reduces compounds in grilled meat that may cause cancer
FOOD SCIENCE Researchers at Kansas State University found that the antioxidants in rosemary inhibit the formation of carcinogenic compounds called heterocyclic amines (HCAs) that form when meat, fish, or poultry is cooked at high temperatures. The herb can reduce the HCA levels by more than half.
PUT IT TOGETHER Add some finely chopped rosemary to dry rubs or marinades. Basil, oregano, sage, and mint can also protect against HCAs.

BROCCOLI + FISH + TOMATO

WHAT IT DOES Slows cancer-cell growth
FOOD SCIENCE Fish contains lots of selenium, a mineral that raises levels of a cancer-fighting enzyme; broccoli has sulforaphane, a chemical that boosts the same enzyme. When scientists combined the two nutrients, they discovered the pairing was 13 times more effective at slowing cancer-cell growth than when each was consumed individually. Add tomatoes and the news gets better: Studies show that prostate tumors grow less in males who eat broccoli

PERFECT PAIR
Match foods and
eat together to
draw out even
more nutrients.

and tomatoes in tandem rather than separately.
PUT IT TOGETHER Enjoy your grilled halibut, salmon, or tuna topped with a tomato salsa and a side of steamed broccoli. Or choose another cruciferous vegetable, such as cabbage or cauliflower.

OATMEAL + STRAWBERRIES

WHAT IT DOES Lowers the likelihood of a stroke or heart attack
FOOD SCIENCE Oats are rich in antioxidants called phenols, which keep free radicals from damaging LDL ("bad" cholesterol). That's good news because the more stable LDL is, the less likely it is to stick to artery walls and cause a heart attack or stroke. Researchers at Tufts University found that these phenols work even harder in the presence of vitamin C (nine ounces of strawberries provides more than your daily need), making LDL twice as secure as when the oat phenols are consumed alone.
PUT IT TOGETHER Have a bowl of high-fiber oatmeal topped with strawberries. Or drink a glass of orange juice to get the same benefits.

TURMERIC + BLACK PEPPER

WHAT IT DOES Reduces muscle inflammation and pain
FOOD SCIENCE The active compound curcumin, contained in the yellow Indian spice turmeric (and curry), reduces the inflammation from exercise-induced muscle damage, according to a 2007 study in the *American Journal of Physiology*. Mixing the spice with black pepper—which contains the active component piperine—significantly increases the absorption of curcumin, upping its anti-inflammatory effects.
PUT IT TOGETHER Use as a dry rub for grilled chicken—which contains protein for muscle repair—for the perfect postrun recovery dinner.

PEANUT BUTTER + BREAD

WHAT IT DOES Promotes muscle growth
FOOD SCIENCE On top of zinc to up your immunity, and heart-healthy fats, peanuts contain amino acids—the building blocks of protein. When added to those present in bread, they form a "complete" protein, providing a foundation for muscle growth and repair—making this the perfect snack before or after training.
PUT IT TOGETHER Wash your sandwich down with a glass of milk. It's rich in conjugated linoleic acid (CLA), a fatty acid compound that has been shown to help increase muscle mass and decrease body fat.

SALMON + SESAME SEEDS + KALE

WHAT IT DOES Builds bone strength
FOOD SCIENCE Sesame seeds and kale are good sources of calcium, as are all dark-green leafy vegetables—essential to maintaining good bone health. The vitamin-D hit found in the salmon—and other fish with natural oils—stimulates the intestinal absorption of this mineral, promoting bone growth. Sesame seeds are also rich in zinc, needed for the enzyme that controls the development of the bone structure.
PUT IT TOGETHER For a bone-building boost, serve sesame-seed-crusted salmon fillets with a portion of lightly steamed kale. If kale is hard to find, then broccoli and spinach are decent replacements.

RED APPLES + GRAPES

WHAT IT DOES Prevents arteries from clogging
FOOD SCIENCE Red apples—particularly their skin—contain high levels of the flavonol quercetin, while grapes' seeds and skins are a good source of catechins. A study reported in the *American Journal of Clinical Nutrition* demonstrated that pairing these two antioxidant compounds together may help improve cardiovascular health by making blood platelets less sticky, reducing the chance of them clumping together and clogging the arteries. Grapes also protect LDL cholesterol from the free radical damage that initiates LDL's artery-damaging actions.
PUT IT TOGETHER Serve in yogurt for breakfast—or pack in a fruit salad with other heart-healthy fruits, such as oranges, grapefruit, and other citrus fruits.

MARJORAM + SALAD

WHAT IT DOES Speeds post-training recovery
FOOD SCIENCE According to a 2005 study in the *British Journal of Nutrition,* adding just a small amount of the aromatic herb marjoram to a salad of lettuce, tomato, onion, carrot, and cucumber boosted its antioxidant value by 200 percent, producing a combination that can help reduce free-radical damage caused by training. Dressing salad with olive oils and wine or apple vinegars also increases the antioxidant capacity.
PUT IT TOGETHER Top your salad with artichoke, beets, and broccoli, which in the same study were found to have the highest antioxidant values of the vegetables tested.

IMAGE: TODD HUFFMAN

FUELING YOUR FIRE

Run out of gas during a long run and you will crash to the pavement. The perfect nutrition strategy of personal mobile pit stops will have you clocking faster times and feeling stronger

> **YOU'VE BEEN RUNNING** for months. You've spent more early mornings in running shoes than you have tucked up in bed; you've done short runs, long runs, quick ones, and slow ones, all of them at paces ranging from "race" to "rather not, thanks." You've burned through three pairs of shoes and set new personal bests along the way. You may be planning to enter a race, or simply to run faster for your own entertainment.

But despite all the hours of hard work, you won't reach that finish line or see the time you were hoping for on your watch if you're not prepared to provide your body with the fuel it needs along the way. A good nutrition strategy is as important to your success as registering for a race on time or tying your laces. The time to start forming your midrun habits is a long time before you're limbering up on the starting line. It should start a few weeks into your schedule of marathon preparation—and should become a habit for all long runs.

WALL TO FALL

Regardless of whether it's a gel, a drink, a bar, or even just sweets that you're knocking back on the move, you're doing it for one very visceral reason—the wall.

The wall is what distance runners hit, traditionally somewhere after 18 miles. They feel light-headed and utterly without energy. In short, they would much prefer to just go home and take a nap than keep on going.

Is this you? And, if so, what happened? How could collapsing into a sofa or a bath become a viable alternative to strong running? When your body senses that your easily accessible reserves of carbohydrate energy have fallen to 40 or 50 percent, it starts to use its fat as a source of fuel. It simply cannot let your blood sugar reserves empty completely, because your brain relies on them.

The trouble is that fat can't be turned into energy nearly as fast as blood sugar can, so your body becomes forced to either slow down or increase its effort dramatically to maintain the same speed. In both cases, you'll find yourself breathing more heavily, because fat conversion requires more oxygen.

"When running you burn through your main source of stored energy—glycogen—very quickly, and the faster you go the more quickly you burn it," says coach Nick Anderson. "With shorter distances, three to six miles, say, you need to remain hydrated for optimal performance, but you don't have to worry

IMAGE: MITCH MANDEL

about completely depleting your carbohydrate stores.

"However, once you're out there for longer than 90 minutes, you can expect to see a depletion of those glycogen stores. You will slow down dramatically and hit the wall."

So, very simply put, if your body runs out of glycogen, it has no fuel left, and to keep running it has to resort to its only other fuel source—stored fats. Processing stored fats requires a lot more oxygen, so you slow down to a jog or even a walk so that less of the oxygen you breathe in goes to your muscles and more is available to break down the energy. From the wall onward, it's a mental battle to the end of your run.

You don't want to hit the wall. It's not a clever name—walls hurt and this one will, too. Fortunately, with the right nutrition you don't have to experience the full horror of the face-brick interface. In fact, by maintaining your glycogen levels, your face need never come near anything vaguely brick-like whatsoever.

"It's a mix of people running too hard and not using the right nutrition," says Anderson. "Someone who has a good nutrition strategy will run even splits throughout a long run."

Fundamentally, your nutrition strategy for any long run is to take in carbohydrates every 40 to 45 minutes that you're on the road. Remember that and stick to it. Whatever distance you're running, if you're going to be running for longer than an hour, you should be putting in some fuel. So for a marathon you may need four to five grams, for a half-marathon perhaps just 2 grams, and on a 10-K most people will have finished before their body needs anything. The

IMAGE: ALAMY

GLOW AHEAD
The right food and drink will fire up your long runs.

EAT UP THE ROAD

Keeping yourself topped off during a race is great, but you've got to start with a full tank of gas. Nutritionist Anita Bean tells you how to fill up the right way.

>THE DAY BEFORE
Your goals for the day before your race are to top off your glycogen stores, stay hydrated, and avoid any pitfalls.

GRAZE Eat little and often throughout the day. Choose high-carbohydrate, low-fat, moderate-protein meals to avoid overburdening your digestive system.

AVOID FEASTING It's not a good idea to gorge the night before a race, as this can wreak havoc on your digestive system and keep you awake at night. You may feel sluggish.

STICK WITH FAMILIAR FOODS Eat only foods that you know agree with you and eat them in normal-sized amounts. Don't try anything new.

AVOID ALCOHOL Sounds obvious, but beyond the hangover, alcohol is a diuretic and, if you have even a bit too much, you will definitely feel well below par the next day.

BEWARE OF THE GAS Avoid gas-forming foods such as baked beans and other legumes, cruciferous vegetables (broccoli, Brussels sprouts, cauliflower), bran cereals, and spicy foods the night before the race.

TAKE TO THE BOTTLE Keep a water bottle handy so you remember to drink regularly throughout the day. This is especially important if you are traveling to the race venue on this day, as it's easy to forget to drink.

>RACE DAY
By now, your muscle glycogen stores should be fully stocked and you should feel ready to go. All that remains to be done before the race is to top off your liver glycogen stores at breakfast, as liver glycogen is normally depleted overnight.

EAT 2–4 HOURS BEFORE A carbohydrate-rich pre-event meal means that you will start exercising fully fueled.

AVOID FRIED FOOD Dodge anything high in fat, such as sausage, bacon, croissants, and pastries. These take longer to digest and will sit heavy.

LIQUID MEAL If you can't eat because of nerves, try a meal-replacement shake, smoothie, or yogurt drink.

DRINK ENOUGH Have at least 16 ounces of water, a sports drink, or diluted fruit juice during the two hours before the race, then another four to eight ounces just before the race.

products are very rapidly absorbed as your body is, understandably, extremely eager to grab what it needs. Just don't wait for a telegram telling you quite how desperately it needs it.

"The classic mistake is to feel woozy and then reach for a drink or a gel," explains Anderson. "They are both packed with sugars as well as complex carbs, both of which work as efficiently as each other. But if you wait until halfway through a marathon to take something in, it's far too late for you to gain the full benefits."

PRODUCTS OF YOUR TIME

What you take in is more than a matter of mere taste. A vast selection of sports-specific products exists, each one vying for that place in your race-day gear bag. But all products are not created equal. You can

IMAGE: GETTY

choose from carbohydrate gels or sports drinks; energy bars or Gummy Bears; every one offers different combinations of nutritional benefit to your body while it's busy setting your personal best for you.

>DRINKS The original performance enhancer is still as good as it always has been. Sports drinks are easy to take in and quickly absorbed, thanks to their liquid format, and they replace the minerals you lose through sweat when you're putting in the hard miles. "Sports drinks are a closer match to your body's fluids, so get to work immediately," says track-and-field coach Chris Husbands. "Intersperse with water, though, as some can be too dense for comfortable digestion."

>GELS If the race organizers will be offering only water on race day, you should tuck some gels into your pockets to ensure that you have access to the energy, electrolytes, and vitamins you'll need along the way. Again, watch your hydration levels. "The efficiency and convenience of gels has resulted in many competitors drinking less during races, causing dehydration and, ironically, decreased performance," says Nick Mitchell, head coach and founder of Ultimate Performance.

>SWEETS The gel and liquid formats have taken over from tablets and chews, being more efficient and easier to digest. That's not to say that something sweet doesn't have its nutritional merits. "Eating jelly beans or Gummy Bears toward the end of a run will do everything a gel does a little slower but taste a lot better," says Anderson. "After all, if you're out there for three to four hours or longer, then you're entitled to a treat."

>BARS In theory, these are the absolute best, packing in the most carbs and therefore providing the most energy. But—and this is noteworthy—they can be difficult to eat on the run. "Cyclists use them all the time because their upper body is static," says Anderson. "And ultrarunners can slow down for the time it takes to eat and digest one." Running puts the stomach walls under constant stress, so giving a runner something solid to deal with can have less than favorable results if you're not used to them.

PREPARE TO SUCCEED

On a pragmatic level, if your body is not well acquainted with the product you choose, then it will be unable to extract the optimal amount of energy at exactly the time when it needs it. So regardless of which carbohydrate source you choose, it's vital to practice on-the-move refueling during training, and especially before a race. Different events have different sponsors, meaning differently branded drink cups are going to be out at the hydration stations.

"You have to make a decision based on the event you're training for and what's available on race day," says Anderson. In the United States, most events have Gatorade or Powerade. Other places may have other brands at their events. "If you're not an elite athlete, you can't put your own drinks out, so you need to practice with what the specific sponsors will be providing around the course."

With that taken care of, take a firm hold of the things you can control—the gels, bars, or sweets you intend to carry with you. Practice taking in your carbohydrates during the long runs of your weekly training, but if you are planning on being at a starting line anytime soon, do it at race pace. Your body needs to adapt to digesting your nutritional weapon of choice at speed, as that's exactly what it will have to do three-quarters of an hour after the start on the big day. Which, it's fair to say, is not a time to give your stomach any surprises.

Finally, on the morning of any race, do yourself and your nutrition strategy a favor—look up. The weather influences more than what shirt you wear. On a hot day you burn through your glycogen more quickly, which means adapting the timings of your fueling to come five to 10 minutes more often, every 30 minutes in extreme cases. But it's not just the scorchers you have to worry about. "On a very cold day, people don't take in very much at all," says Anderson. "They don't think they're sweating, but it's just that the moisture is being absorbed by technical clothing. On a very cold day you still need a good hydration and nutrition strategy."

Pick your product, practice with it in training, and stick to your strategy. The rules of midrace nutrition are that simple and are based upon even more straightforward biological principles. Your body uses energy to power you onward; if that energy runs out, you will have nothing to go on with besides grim determination. After all, grim determination, though sometimes enough, is nowhere near as tasty.

SPECIAL EXTRAS

Energy drinks or gels will contain glucose, maltodextrin, and perhaps fructose to deliver fast energy. Sodium and potassium are often also present to replace lost electrolytes and to speed rehydration. However, many products on the market now include these extra ingredients designed to enhance performance:

CAFFEINE As evidence stacks up that caffeine can boost athletic performance, more manufacturers are including it in their energy products. Don't worry—it won't dehydrate you, and it may genuinely help you run faster.

GUARANA This stimulant is a Brazilian plant. It contains caffeine and acts in a similar way.

B VITAMINS (including niacin, thiamin, and pantothenic acid). This group of vitamins helps your body release energy from food and drink, so it is used during races.

MINERALS (often magnesium and calcium). These help with muscle contractions and nerve function.

ANTIOXIDANTS Vitamins A (including carotenes), C, and E are antioxidant vitamins that may be included in your energy products. They'll also help protect your immunity.

PROTEIN Though carbs are the best energy source for runners, protein can also be used to fuel your muscles, and it helps protect them from damage caused by long sessions.

AMINO ACIDS These are the building blocks of protein and are used for energy. Some products contain branched chain amino acids (BCAAs), which may prevent mental fatigue toward the end of a long run.

10 WAYS TO AVOID INJURY

Even if you train right, injury can strike. But if you obey these commandments, you can stack the odds against it in your favor

> **MOST RUNNERS KNOW ABOUT INJURIES.** They're almost part of the game. Run long enough or hard enough, and you'll probably come down with an ache that will temporarily sideline you.

Fortunately, most running injuries are short-term. After a few days or weeks of rest, you can return to your regular routine. Still, there is a better way: Don't get injured in the first place. If you adopt the principles outlined on these pages, you'll have a reasonable chance of running in good health indefinitely. Ignore them, and...well, you know. You reap what you sow.

1 WARM UP, COOL DOWN

When you first get up in the morning, your muscles and soft tissue are tight. In fact, at that time, your muscles are generally about 10 percent shorter than their normal resting lengths. As you move around, they stretch out. Then when you start to exercise, your muscles stretch even more, to about 10 percent longer than their resting lengths. This means you have a 20 percent change in muscle length from the time you get out of bed until your muscles are well warmed up.

According to the basic laws of physics, muscles work more efficiently when they are longer; they can exert more force with less effort. This means, too, that longer muscles are much less prone to injury.

Make it a habit to warm up before a run or race. Pedal for a few minutes indoors on a stationary bike, or skip with a rope for a few turns before you head down the road. If you'd rather warm up on the run, begin with a walk or a slow jog and gradually speed up.

Cooling down can also help you avoid injury. An easy jog after a hard session or race has been shown to speed recovery by helping remove any lactic acid that may have accumulated. It also gently brings your muscles back to a resting state.

A good warmup and cooldown are especially important before and after a hard run in which you push your muscles to their limits. The extra time you spend warming up your muscles before a training run or race and cooling down afterward is worth the effort in improved efficiency and decreased risk of injury.

2 STRETCH OUT

Without flexibility, you are an injury waiting to happen. Tight muscles cannot go through their full range of motion properly. Lack of flexibility is probably the biggest cause of Achilles tendinitis and is a major factor in plantar fasciitis and shinsplints. Although your hamstrings tend to be the workhorses, don't forget to stretch the fronts of your legs as well.

Stretching is not the same as warming up. Trying to stretch "short" muscles may cause injury. The best time to stretch is after a run, when your muscles are warm and elongated. Make stretching part of your routine every day.

3 CHILL OUT

Let your training schedule be your guide—but never your jailer. One of the surest ways to become injured is to train hard on a day when you're tired or feeling soreness or the pain of an injury about to happen. If you feel fatigued or overly sluggish, or if you notice twinges of muscular pain, ease up. You will not lose fitness over a few days of rest. Remember that any schedule is built on the assumption that you aren't experiencing pain. Listen to your body.

IMAGES: STEVE BOYLE, GETTY

4 KNOW YOUR GROUND

To stay injury-free, mix your training surfaces to match your type of run.

1 ASPHALT ROADS

Firmer training surfaces absorb less energy, meaning more power and speed from every push off the ground. Good for PR-chasers, but hard roads are also hard on the shins and knees.
STEP TO IT Avoid pounding the pavement for long runs and do fartlek sessions, using lampposts as markers to speed up or slow down.

2 SYNTHETIC TRACK

Perfect for precision speedwork, and more cushioned than asphalt. But the curves can tighten calf muscles and irritate your iliotibial (IT) bands.
STEP TO IT Run at 90 percent of maximum effort on the straight sections, slowing to a recovery jog on the curve before repeating for four or five laps.

3 LOOSE EARTH

A medium-soft surface, rural dirt roads lower the risk of overuse injuries such as ITB syndrome. Gravel is also worth a try. More resistant than grass, and softer than asphalt, it's another great midway surface.
STEP TO IT Take to the trails for your weekly long runs, running at a minute or two slower than target marathon pace.

4 GRASS

The softest option is far less strenuous on the joints and bones, because it absorbs most of the energy from your footfall. The uneven surface also makes stabilizer muscles work—just tread carefully.
STEP TO IT Play the field for your long run, and/or two or three maintenance runs a week of about three to seven miles at conversational pace.

5 SAND

Use sand for strength training. Italian researchers found that athletes who did four weeks of sand-based plyometrics improved their sprint times as much as those who trained on grass, but with less soreness.
STEP TO IT Do 15 squat jumps to work your calves and quads: Stand with feet shoulder-width apart, hands on your head. Squat deeply, then push up and jump as high as you can.

6 TREADMILL

Treadmill running is about keeping stable. Your stride lengthens, foot turnover decreases, and muscles don't work so hard. But increase the incline and you boost power output from quads, hamstrings, and calves.
STEP TO IT After a two-minute jog at a 0.5 percent incline, up the ante gradually every 20 seconds. Do six minutes before reducing the incline in 20-second increments.

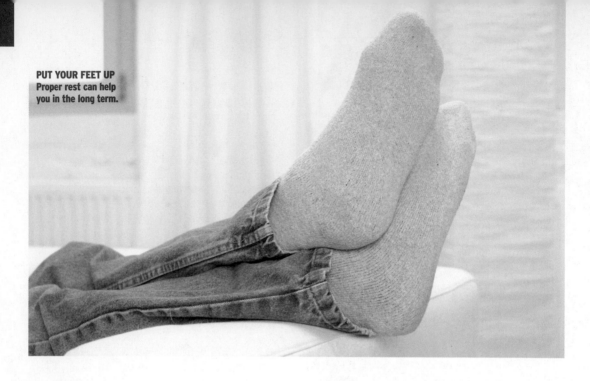

PUT YOUR FEET UP
Proper rest can help
you in the long term.

5 BACK OFF

If you train hard every day, you'll wear your body down rather than build it up. You need to recover after a tough training session or a race—give your muscles a chance to mend and stock up on glycogen for your next hard effort. This is why most experts recommend that you never schedule hard sessions two days in a row. Give yourself at least one day of easy running or rest between hard efforts. If you run fast one day, train slowly the next. If you run long one day, plan a short one for the following day. This is the hard/easy method of training.

Just as some people need more sleep than others, some people need more recovery. You may discover that your body performs best when you rest for two days after a hard training session. Or you may even need three easy days. Experiment with various combinations of hard and easy runs and compare the benefits of easy running versus rest or a different form of training. Which leads us to the next point...

6 BRANCH OUT

Runners once took a run-or-nothing approach to their sport, and many still do, believing that other sports cannot benefit their running and may in fact hurt it. The wiser runner explores other options, both to supplement running during periods of good health and as a substitute for running if they are injured.

Participating in another sport a couple of times a week gives your feet and legs respite from the constant pounding of running and strengthens muscles that running does not exercise. In both of these ways, cross-training can help protect you from injury.

Replace an easy run or rest day with a cross-training workout. After all, it is often not total rest that your body needs but merely a break from the specialized action of running. The more muscles you can involve, the less likely you are to suffer an overuse injury. Additionally, by working more of your major muscle groups, you improve overall fitness.

If you do become injured through running and have been cross-training regularly, you will have an activity to turn to that will keep you fit while you recover. Overuse symptoms such as soreness or injuries caused by too much shock or jarring can be relieved through swimming or cycling. By using a stair climber, rowing machine, or cross-country ski machine, you can take the stress off an injured area and still benefit.

7 SPACE YOUR RACES

Racing pushes the limits of your speed and endurance, and too much racing can push you beyond your ability to avoid injury. Racing is hard, so give yourself plenty of time to recover after each event.

The general rule is to take one easy day or rest day for each mile you have raced, and certainly don't race

IMAGE: ALAMY

again until that period has passed. For example, allow one easy week following a hard 10-K and an easy month after completing a marathon. Top marathoners believe that they can run only two or three good marathons in a year—the grueling event takes that great a toll.

8 WRITE IT DOWN

Keeping a training log of your daily runs may seem compulsive or boring, but charting your distance, pace and course, the weather, and how you feel can give you perspective and can help you see if you've been training too little or too much.

Review your log weekly with a critical eye. Pretend it's someone else's training program. You may be amazed at the training errors you find. Correct these errors, and you'll become a better runner—and one more likely to stay injury-free.

9 BUT IF YOU DO GET INJURED...

...come back slowly—much more slowly than you might think necessary.

After a layoff or an injury, your bones and joints are just not ready for any pounding. They have become somewhat soft and lazy, and it takes time to build them to the point at which they can take the forces of running without becoming re-injured.

Furthermore, it's possible that your injury hasn't healed completely, making you more susceptible to re-injury. If you stress your body too much too soon, the same symptoms are likely to reappear, and you could end up with a more long-term problem.

Depending on how long your layoff is, you might need a walk/run regimen. Although you would rather eat asphalt than be caught walking, do it anyway. You'll gain fitness without the hard pounding of running.

If you try to take shortcuts or cheat your body's natural timetable, you're asking for trouble. You simply cannot rush your recovery. As you become stronger and start to run regularly, increase your weekly distance by no more than 10 percent.

10 EAT WELL

During a layoff, many runners cut back on their diets to prevent weight gain. This isn't necessary. You need extra nutrients to help your body mend the injured area and to fuel your training once you renew your running program. If you do gain a few pounds during your recovery period, they'll just melt away when you begin running again. So eat, and train, wisely and you'll keep running year after year without injury.

THE MOST COMMON ROUTES TO INJURY

Sometimes avoiding injury is about what you don't do. These are some of the most common errors made by new and experienced runners alike.

WEARING NEW SHOES ON RACE DAY This is tempting, because new running shoes have a slipper-like feel. That might remain the case for a short while, but resist it. A plethora of foot and lower-limb problems are just a few miles away.
PREVENTION Break them in first.

WEARING OLD SHOES It's easy to judge wear by the state of the outsole and the upper, rather than (correctly) by the compression of the midsole. Joint or shin soreness is the most obvious result and is a sign that your shoes need replacing.
PREVENTION Log the miles you've run in each pair of shoes and change them every 500 to 600 miles.

WEARING THE WRONG SHOES This could either be a model unsuited to your gait and foot, or a shoe inappropriate to the type of running you're doing. Either way, you have a problem.
PREVENTION If you don't know what you're doing, shop at a specialty running retailer.

IGNORING PAIN
You have to learn to separate good pain, associated with increasing fitness, from bad pain, which tends to be unfamiliar, infrequent, and localized in one area of the body. It is an early warning sign of injury.
PREVENTION Ease off, and seek medical help where necessary.

STARTING TREATMENT WITHOUT DIAGNOSIS Okay, so you have an injury, you know it's a bad one, and you feel you know how to solve it. So you start treatment. The trouble is that you're a runner, not a medical expert. You may have misdiagnosed your problem and started the wrong treatment.
PREVENTION See a professional.

NOT DRINKING ENOUGH Dehydration affects your health and performance whenever you run.
PREVENTION Drink fluid a little at a time, and often throughout the day, every day.

RUNNER'S WORLD PROMOTION

5-K READY?

202255002

Start your 5-K training with a FREE GIFT on us! SCAN NOW ›

Get the free mobile app at Scanlife.com

INJURY CLINIC

If you suffer from any of these
five common running injuries,
our doctors are in—
and can help heal you

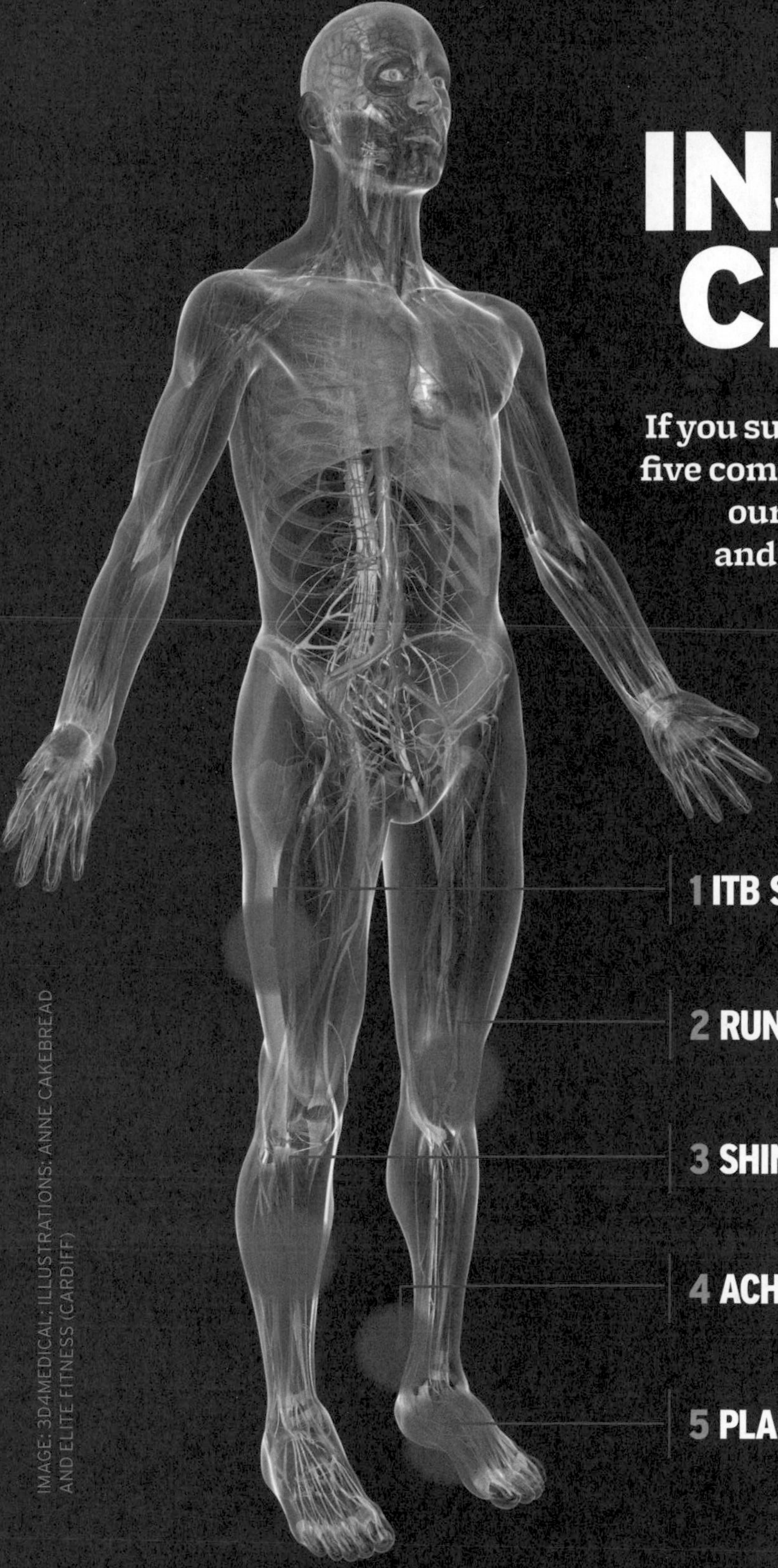

1 ITB SYNDROME

2 RUNNER'S KNEE

3 SHINSPLINTS

4 ACHILLES TENDINITIS

5 PLANTAR FASCIITIS

IMAGE: 3D4MEDICAL; ILLUSTRATIONS: ANNE CAKEBREAD AND ELITE FITNESS (CARDIFF)

1 ILIOTIBIAL-BAND SYNDROME

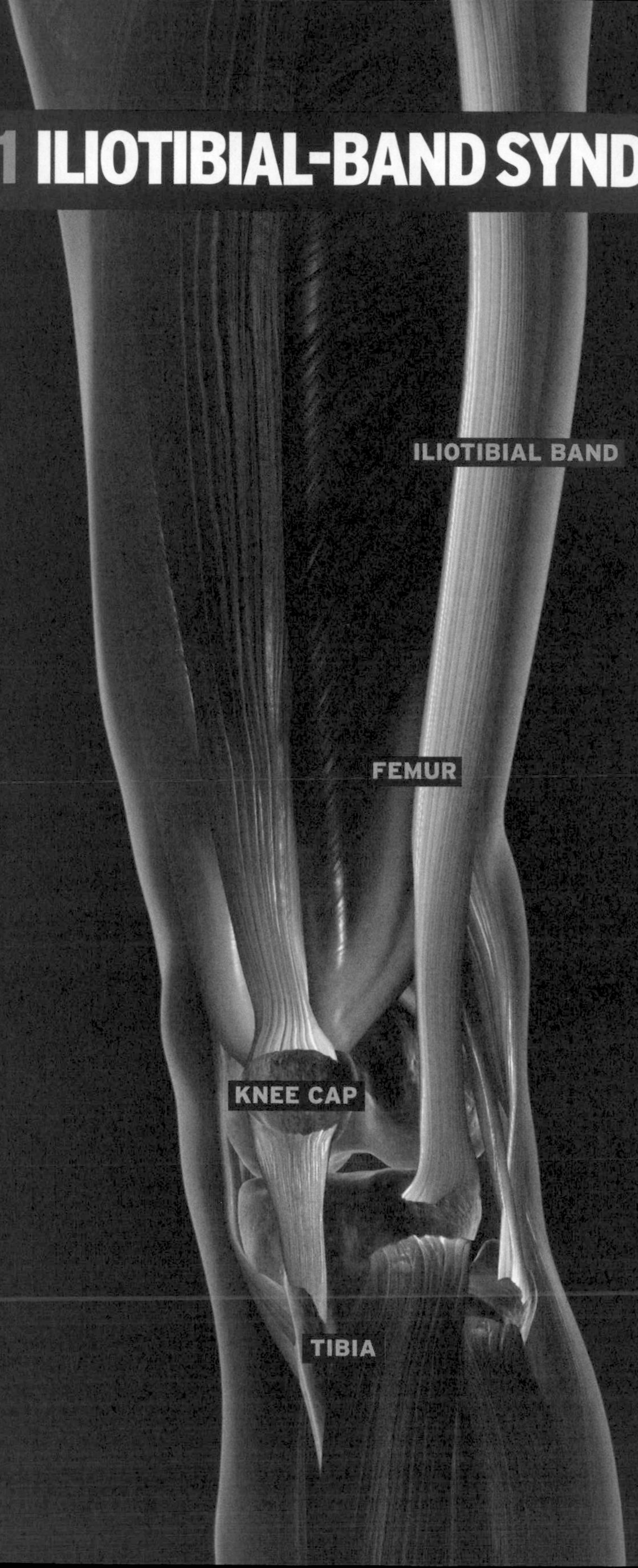

ILIOTIBIAL BAND

FEMUR

KNEE CAP

TIBIA

PAIN, EXPLAINED

Australian performance coach Carlyle Jenkins explains why your knee feels like it's got a stake driven through it.

ANATOMY LESSON

Your iliotibial band (ITB) is a ligament-like structure that starts at your pelvis and runs along the outside of your thigh to the top of your shinbone (tibia). When you run, your ITB rubs back and forth over a bony outcrop on your femur, which helps stabilize it.

BAND AID

If you have poor running mechanics or muscle imbalance, put on weight, or started running hills, then your ITB can track out of line, slipping out of the groove created by the bony outcrop.

SWELLING

As it tracks out of its natural alignment, it rubs against other structures in your leg, creating friction on the band. This results in inflammation (but no swelling) and a click when you bend your knee.

HOLD UP

The scarring thickens and tightens the ITB, and limits the blood flow to it. If you continue to run, you'll feel a stinging sensation. This can make you limp after a run.

IMAGE: 3D4MEDICAL; ILLUSTRATIONS: ANNE CAKEBREAD AND ELITE FITNESS (CARDIFF)

CAUSE & EFFECT

Why it happens
and how to spot it

WHAT CAUSES IT?

According to research in the *Clinical Journal of Sports Medicine*, these are the roots of the problem:

>>Inadequate warmup before running

>>Increasing distance, running too quickly, or excessive downhill running

>>High or low arches in your feet that cause your feet to overpronate

>>Uneven leg length

>>Bowed legs

>>Excessive wear on the outside heel edge of a running shoe

>>Weak hip abductors

>>Running on a banked surface, such as the shoulder of a road or track

SPOT IT!

According to Jenkins, you're a likely ITB sufferer if you experience one of the following signs:

>>A sharp or burning pain on the outside of the knee. The symptoms may subside shortly after a run is over, but will return with the next run.

>>You feel tenderness on the outside of your knee if you apply pressure, especially when bending.

>>You may have problems standing on one leg on the affected side, usually due to a weak gluteus medius.

HOW TO REHABILITATE IT

Decrease your training load by 50 percent and apply the principles of R.I.C.E. (rest, ice, compression, and elevation), then use some of these rehabilitation tips from Jenkins.

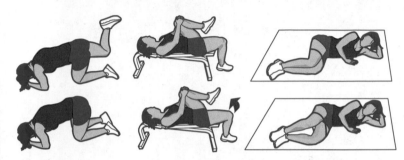

DONKEY KICKS

1 Get on all fours, resting your body weight on your knees and flattening your forearms on the floor into a position similar to that of The Sphinx.
2 Keep your right knee bent as you slowly lift your right leg up behind you so your foot rises toward the ceiling.
3 Hold that position for one second, then slowly return to the start. Perform four sets of 12 repetitions on each leg.
WHY This move strengthens your gluteus maximus and medius. Research in the journal *Physical Therapy in Sport* has found that these muscles are vital for keeping your ITB strong.

LYING ITB STRETCH

1 Sit on the edge of a bench or firm bed. Lay your torso back and pull the unaffected leg to your chest to flatten your lower back.
2 With your affected leg flat to the bench, maintain a 90-degree bend in that knee. Shift that knee as far inward to the side (toward your other foot) as possible.
3 Hold this position for 30 seconds and repeat four times on each leg.
WHY "The ITB is difficult to elongate, as it doesn't have nerves that allow you to feel if you're actually stretching it. You might not feel this move in the ITB, but it does isolate the band," says Jenkins.

SIDE-LYING CLAMSHELL

1 Lie on your side, bending knees and hips to 90 degrees. Wrap a resistance band around both thighs.
2 Lift your top knee up toward the ceiling, making sure that the insides of both feet stay together.
3 Perform 10 to 15 reps, or until you get a burn in the outside of your hip.
WHY "This move works your gluteus medius (on the outer surface of the pelvis). This muscle prevents your thigh from buckling inward when you run, which is the root of ITB aches," says Richard Scrivener, a running and injury lecturer at Premier Training International.

HOW LONG UNTIL YOU'RE RECOVERED

According to performance coach Carlyle Jenkins, these are the recovery rates of iliotibial-band syndrome, depending on the severity of your injury.

>>**MILD INJURY**
100% after 2-4 weeks

>>**AVERAGE INJURY**
100% after 7-8 weeks

>>**SEVERE INJURY**
100% after 9-24 weeks

2 RUNNER'S KNEE

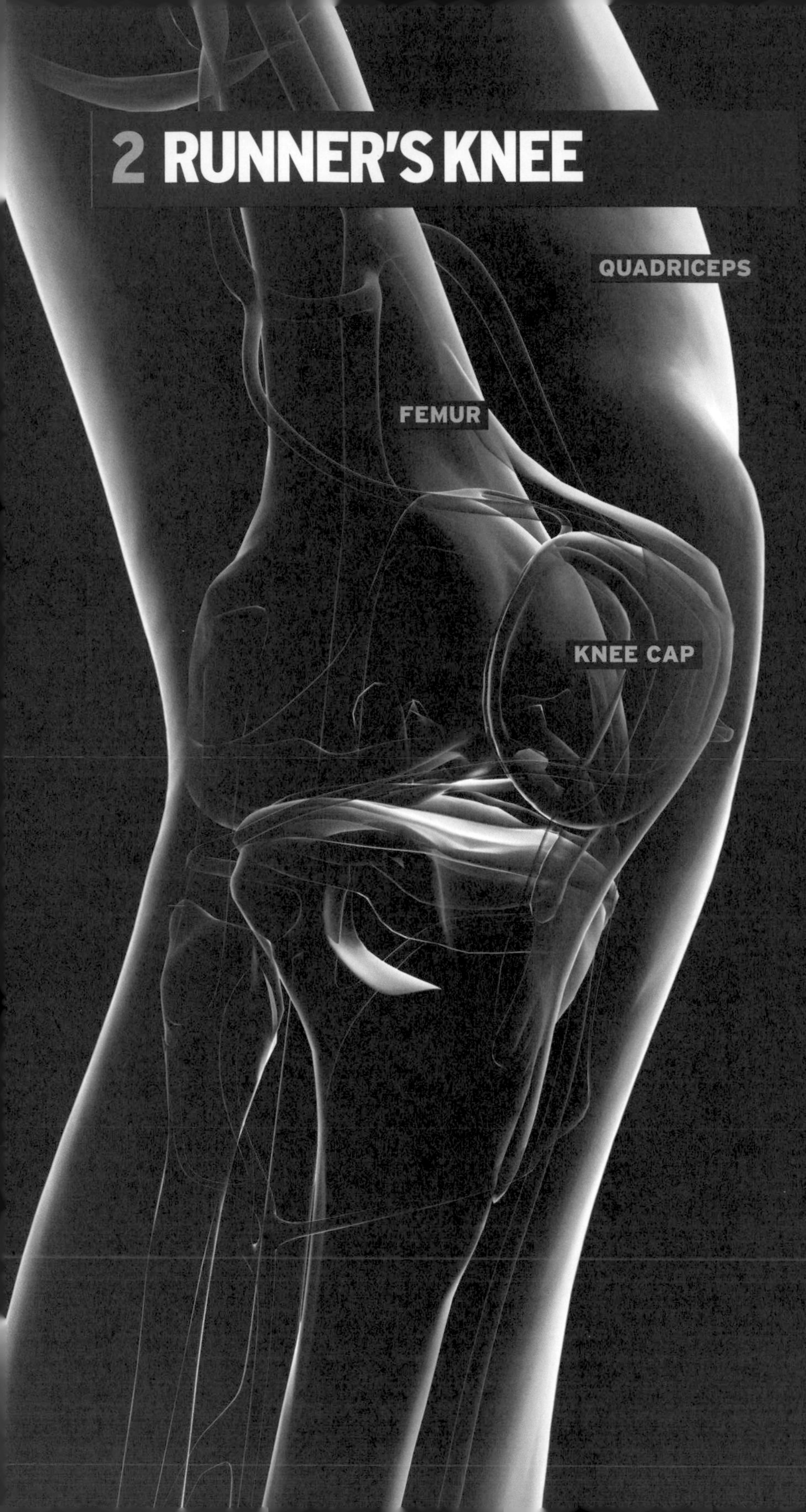

QUADRICEPS

FEMUR

KNEE CAP

PAIN, EXPLAINED

Ross Sherman, senior exercise physiologist and sports science consultant at Kingston University, London, explains what causes it.

WORKING ORDER

Your quads, the thigh muscles above the knee, hold your kneecap in place. When you run, your kneecap moves up and down your thighbone (femur) without touching it.

FAULTY FUNCTIONING

If your quads are weak or you have poor foot mechanics, your kneecap will move left and right, creating pressure, friction, and irritation. As you keep logging miles and repeatedly stride out your misaligned steps, your kneecap rubs against the end of the thighbone.

WORN DOWN

This wobbling and rubbing grinds down the cartilage underneath your kneecap so that it becomes rough, like sandpaper. This makes your kneecap unable to bend smoothly and efficiently.

SYMPTOMS

When this happens, you'll experience a dull, aching pain under or around the front of your kneecap. The pinch will be the worst when running downhill, walking down stairs, squatting, or sitting with a bent knee.

IMAGE: 304 MEDICAL ILLUSTRATIONS: ANNE CAKEBREAD AND ELITE FITNESS (CARDIFF)

CAUSE & EFFECT
Why it happens and how to spot it

WHAT CAUSES IT?
According to research in the *Journal of Sports Medicine*, these are the main culprits:
>> Weak quadriceps and hips
>> Overuse or a sudden increase in mileage
>> Knock knees
>> Tight hamstrings or calves
>> Overpronation or supination
>> Running on uneven surfaces
>> A previous injury, such as a dislocation of the kneecap

SPOT IT!
Here's a self-assessment test for runner's knee:
>> Sit on a chair and rest your stretched-out leg on another chair in front of you. Tense your quad.
>> Gently squeeze above the offending knee with your right hand and push on the outside of the kneecap with your left hand.
>> If you feel a scorching twinge, then you've got runner's knee.
>> "If pain radiates into your back, hips, or feet when you do this, see a sports-medicine specialist, who can examine you," says Richard Scrivener, a running and injury lecturer at Premier Training International.

HOW TO REHABILITATE IT

After applying the rules of R.I.C.E. (rest, ice, compression, and elevation), take a rest from all sports for one to two weeks. Then do these moves from Sherman two or three times a week.

  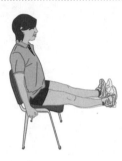

LYING LEG LIFTS
1 Lie flat on back. Bend your left knee at 90 degrees, keeping your foot flat on floor.
2 Keep your right leg straight and lift it to the height of the left knee.
3 Hold for five to 10 seconds and repeat five to 10 times on both legs.
WHY "When running, your body weight lands on a near-straightened knee," says Sherman. "This move strengthens your quads—the muscle that absorbs the blow—in the position they receive the impact. This stabilizes the injured knee."

STABILITY-BALL HALF SQUATS
1 Put a stability ball between your lower back and a wall.
2 Bend your knees to lower yourself toward the floor. Stop when your knees are bent at 90 degrees.
3 Straighten your legs to rise to the top without locking your knees.
WHY "Do four to five sets of 12 repetitions to strengthen your quads, lower back, glutes, and core. These muscles work together to teach your knees to start bending through their natural range of movement," says Sherman.

FOOT TURNS
1 Sit in a chair and stretch both legs out straight in front of you, feet pointed straight up toward the ceiling.
2 Turn both feet out as far as possible. Hold for 12 seconds while tensing your quads.
3 Turn them inward for 12 seconds. That's one set; do six sets.
WHY "You'll strengthen your outer and inner quads, building the cartilage on either side of the knee cap, which stops it from tracking out of line in the future," says Sherman.

HOW LONG UNTIL YOU'RE RECOVERED

According to Ross Sherman, these are the recovery rates, depending on the severity of your injury. If your injury is only mild, you can recover in six weeks, as long as you take his advice to rest up for the first two weeks and do his rehabilitation exercises to help overcome the injury. If the injury is particularly severe, it could take up to six months to recover.

>> **MILD INJURY**
40%–50% better after 1–2 weeks
60%–75% better after a month
100% better after 6–8 weeks

>> **SEVERE INJURY**
30%–40% better after 2–3 weeks
50%–60% better after 2 months
100% better after 4–6 months

3 SHINSPLINTS

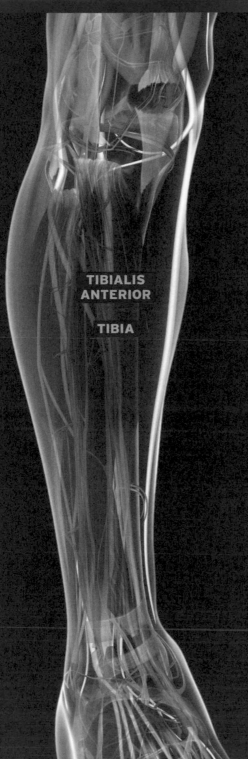

TIBIALIS ANTERIOR

TIBIA

PAIN, EXPLAINED

Sports rehab specialist Jenkins explains the reasons for that persistent ache in your shins.

TOO MUCH TOO SOON

Shinsplints are an overuse injury. The muscle most affected is the tibialis anterior, stretching from your knee to your ankle. A new or excessive running stress can irritate it.

TAKE HEED

By resting and applying our rehab tips when you feel mild tenderness in your shinbone (tibia), you'll eliminate further damage. But if you soldier on with more miles, then you'll create microtears.

IT HURTS

You'll feel a razor-sharp pain on the outer edges of the mid region of your lower leg, next to the shinbone. The aching area can measure four to six inches, and the pain often subsides after warming up and returns after the workout is finished.

SEE A DOC

Worst-case scenario is that the swelling in the muscle and sheath continues unabated, increasing the pressure in the sheath to intolerable levels. This can lead to Compartment Syndrome, a condition that can require surgery.

CAUSE & EFFECT
Why it happens and how to spot it

WHAT CAUSES IT?

The Mayo Clinic found that shinsplints are caused by an overload on the shinbone and connective tissues, which attach your muscles to the bone. This overload is often caused by:
>>Running downhill
>>Running on a slanted or tilted surface, such as some crowned roads
>>Running in worn-out footwear
>>Doing sports with frequent starts and stops, such as squash or tennis
>>Shinsplints can also be caused by training too hard, too fast, or for too long.
>>Overpronation; the tibia is forced to twist in the opposite direction. Too much twisting can lead to shinsplints.
>>A return to exercise after a long hiatus

SPOT IT!

The Mayo Clinic found that the tell-tale signs of shinsplints are:
>>Tenderness, soreness, or pain along the outer part of your lower leg
>>Mild swelling of the muscles around your shinbone
>>At first, the pain may end when you've finished your warmup. Eventually, however, the pain may be continuous.

HOW TO REHABILITATE IT

Dramatically decrease your training load by 90 to 95 percent and apply the principles of R.I.C.E. (rest, ice, compression, and elevation), then use some of these rehabilitation tips from sports rehab specialist Jenkins once a day.

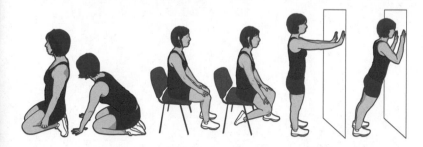

KNEELING STRETCH

1 Get into a kneeling position with your toes tucked under so that your weight is resting on the balls of your feet and you are sitting on the back of your ankles.
2 Lean forward and rest your fingers on the ground in front of you.
3 Gently sit back onto your heels so that your ankles almost flatten against the floor. Hold for 30 seconds and repeat as needed.
WHY "This move stretches the muscles and connective tissue in the front of your legs and will alleviate some of the pressure in the painful part of your shin," says Jenkins.

SEATED STRETCH

1 Sit on a chair with your feet hip-width apart on the floor and place your hands on your knees.
2 Bend your right leg behind you under the chair and rest the top part of your foot on the floor.
3 Push your foot into the floor and press down gently on your right knee with your right hand. Hold that position for 30 seconds, then switch legs and do the same again.
WHY "This move is very efficient at isolating and loosening your shin muscles and can be done at your desk at work several times during the day," says Jenkins.

STANDING STRETCH

1 Stand with your feet hip-width apart at arm's length from a wall.
2 Place your hands on the wall and keep your feet and knees straight.
3 Lean as far forward as possible while keeping your feet flat. Stop leaning when you feel an intense stretch and hold for 30 seconds.
WHY "If the muscles at the back of your calves become overly tight, this can worsen and even cause shinsplints," says Jenkins. "This move gives these muscles a comprehensive stretch and resets the muscles of your lower leg into the correct position for healing to begin."

HOW LONG UNTIL YOU'RE RECOVERED

An online poll on the fitness Web site attackpoint.org found that these were the expected recovery rates for shinsplints.

>>**MILD INJURY**
100% after 1-2 weeks

>>**AVERAGE INJURY**
100% after 7-8 weeks

>>**SEVERE INJURY**
100% after 9-24 weeks

4 ACHILLES TENDINITIS

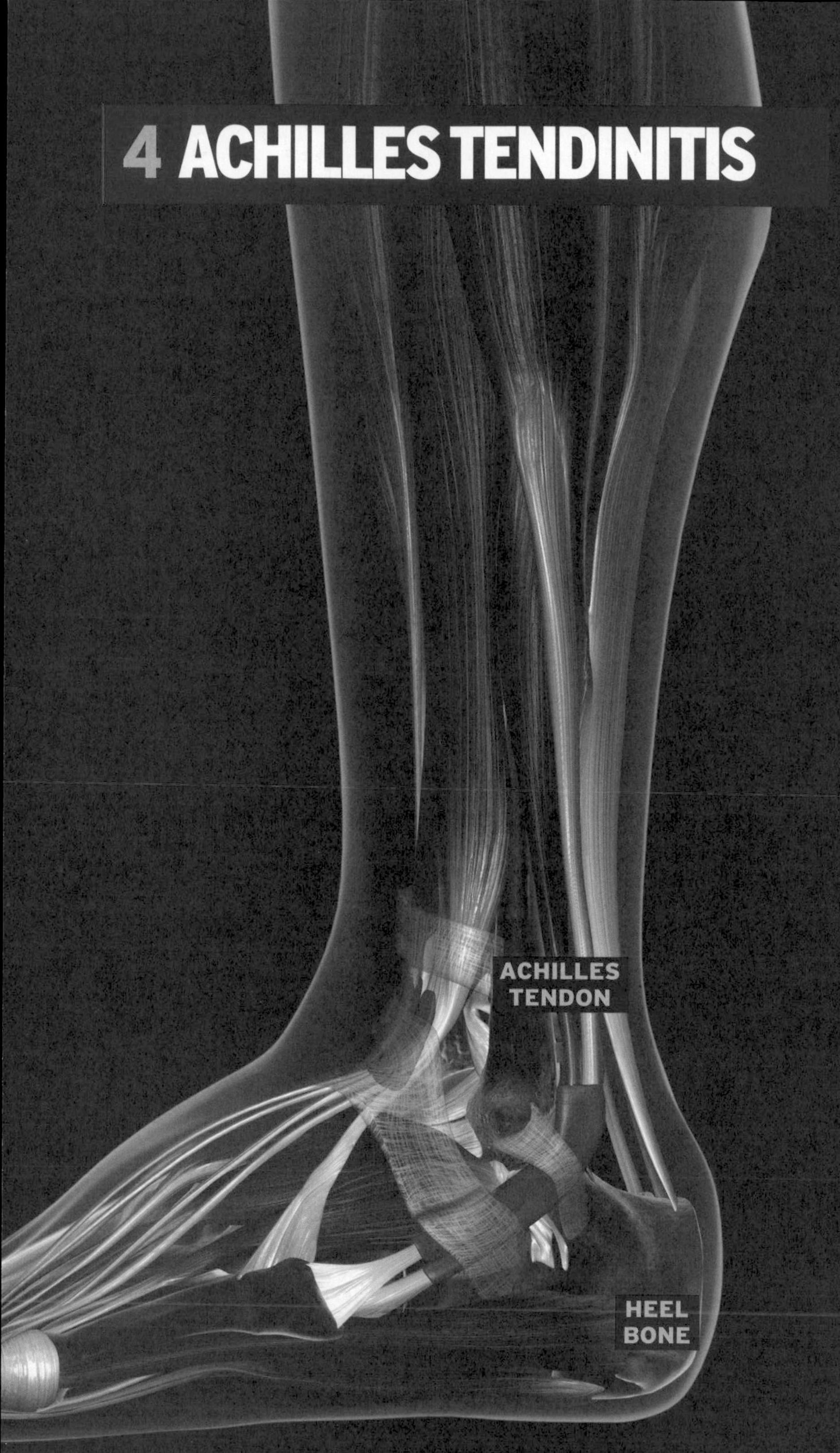

ACHILLES TENDON

HEEL BONE

PAIN, EXPLAINED

Sports performance expert Carlyle Jenkins explains why your Achilles tendon aches.

HARD AT WORK

The Achilles tendon connects the calf muscles to the heel bone. It's the thick, springy tissue just above the heel and is used when you walk, run, jump, or push up on your toes. Injury can occur if you up training frequency or intensity.

OVERLOADED

Achilles tendinitis is an overuse injury where small stresses accumulate and damage the tendon. This strain is increased if you're inflexible or you overpronate.

FIRST RESPONSE

The inflammation is often at the narrow point of the tendon just above the heel area. This is because that area has the smallest blood supply, which slows the healing time considerably. Rest to avoid further pain.

SORE SPOT

You'll feel an ache at the back of your ankle and a burning or piercing pain. You'll experience redness on the tendon and/or severe pain when you take your first few steps in the morning or after sitting for a while. This will subside as you move around.

CAUSE &
EFFECT
Why it happens
and how to spot it

The American Academy
of Orthopaedic Surgeons
says these can trigger
Achilles tendinitis:
>>Rapidly increasing your
running mileage or speed
>>Adding hill running or
stair climbing to your
training routine
>>Starting up too quickly
after a layoff from exercise
>>Trauma caused by
sudden and/or hard
contraction of your
calf muscles when putting
out extra effort, such as
in a final sprint
>>Overuse resulting from a
natural lack of flexibility in
your calf muscles
>>Flattening of the arch
of your foot can place extra
stress on your Achilles.

Research at the Mayo Clinic
found that it's likely you
have Achilles tendinitis if
you suffer with one or more
of these symptoms:
>>Dull ache or pain on the
tendon when pushing off
your foot during walking or
when rising onto your toes
>>Tenderness of your
Achilles tendon
>>Stiffness that lessens
as your tendon warms up
>>Mild swelling or a
"bump" on your tendon
>>A crackling or creaking
sound when you touch or
move your Achilles tendon

HOW TO REHABILITATE IT

Apply the principles of R.I.C.E. (rest, ice, compression, and elevation) and take a break from all weight-bearing sporting activities, including running, for at least two weeks. Then do these scientifically backed stretching and strengthening moves once a day.

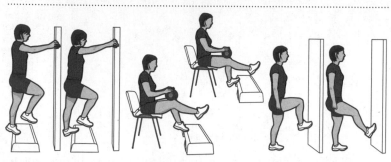

ECCENTRIC STRAIGHT-LEG CALF LOWERING

1 Stand with the balls of your feet on the edge of a step. Hold on to a support if necessary.
2 Rise up onto your toes, then remove the unaffected leg from the step so you're holding the tiptoe position on only the sore leg.
3 Take five seconds to lower your affected heel as far down as is comfortable. Do three sets of 15 twice a day.
WHY A study at the University Hospital of Northern Sweden found that 12 weeks of this and the next exercise combined could eradicate Achilles pain.

ECCENTRIC BENT-LEG CALF LOWERING

1 Sit on the edge of a chair with your legs bent in front of you. Place a weight on top of your thighs and rest the balls of your feet on a ledge or step.
2 Rise up onto your toes, then remove the unaffected leg from the step so you're on tiptoes on the sore leg.
3 Take five seconds to lower your affected heel as far downward as is comfortable. Do three sets of 15 twice a day.
WHY The Swedish researchers noted that doing this exercise with a bent leg forces your deep calf muscle to work, which strengthens the major calf muscles needed to heal Achilles tendinitis.

WALL STRETCH

1 Stand with both feet parallel to each other, facing a wall at about arm's length away.
2 Put the affected foot on the wall at knee height and try to press its heel against the wall.
3 Do not lean toward the wall. Lift your chest until you are standing straight. Hold this position for three minutes on each leg, three times a day.
WHY A study in the journal *Foot & Ankle International* found that holding an Achilles tendon stretch for this exact period of time (three minutes on each leg) helped reduce pain.

HOW LONG UNTIL YOU'RE RECOVERED

According to sports performance specialist Carlyle Jenkins, these are the recovery rates of Achilles tendinitis, depending on the severity of your injury.

>>**MILD INJURY**
100% after 1-2 weeks

>>**AVERAGE INJURY**
100% after 7-8 weeks

>>**SEVERE INJURY**
100% after 42-160 weeks

5 PLANTAR FASCIITIS

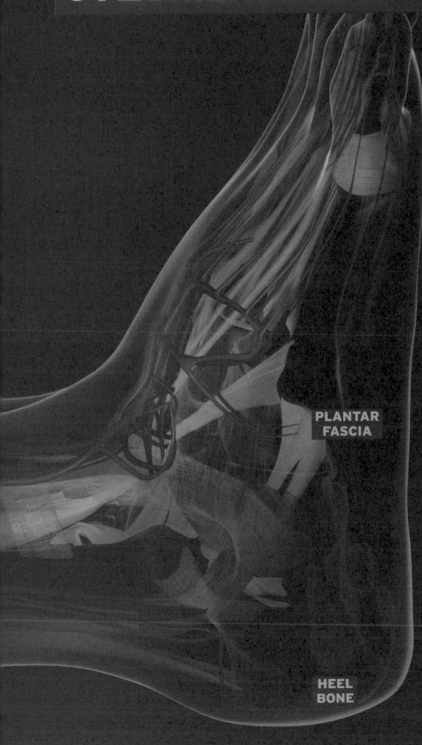

PLANTAR FASCIA

HEEL BONE

PAIN, EXPLAINED

Exercise physiologist Ross Sherman explains why your foot aches.

FOOT WORK

The plantar fascia is a thick broad band of tissue that runs along the bottom of your foot. It supports your foot's arch and acts like a shock-absorbing bowstring.

DAMAGED

When an abnormally high load is forced on it, you get a small split in this tissue. This is an overuse injury, so you won't remember one incident where you damaged your heel. You've sown the seeds if you've increased your training or started running hill sprints.

OVERNIGHT SENSATION

Initially, the rip will create only mild discomfort, which you probably won't even notice. But when you sleep, your body starts the repair process, making the plantar fascia stiff. Upon waking, it will be inflexible. When you take your first strides, you'll stretch and tear it slightly.

PROGRESSIVE PAIN

The tear can lead to additional micro-tearing, which results in the stinging pain at the base of your heel pad, which can last all day if you're on your feet.

CAUSE & EFFECT
Why it happens
and how to spot it

WHAT CAUSES IT?

The American Academy of Orthopaedic Surgeons cites these as the root of plantar fasciitis:

>> A job that requires you to stand for long periods
>> Poor foot mechanics, flat feet, or high arches
>> Being overweight—this places additional pressure on your plantar fascia
>> Tight calves that limit the amount you can flex your ankles
>> An aggressive increase in training load or exertion
>> Arthritis can cause inflammation in the tendons at the bottom of your foot.
>> Diabetes increases your risk, as diabetics have less blood going to their feet.
>> Poor or worn-out shoes

SPOT IT!

Research at the Mayo Clinic found that it's likely you have plantar fasciitis if you experience one or more of the following symptoms:

>> A sharp pain in the inside of the bottom of your heel that may spread under the arch of your foot
>> Heel pain when you wake, stand, or climb stairs
>> Heel pain after long periods of standing or after getting up
>> Heel pain after, but not usually during, exercise
>> Mild swelling in the heel

HOW TO REHABILITATE IT

Rest from all weight-bearing sporting activities, such as running, for at least two to three weeks. Then do these stretching and strengthening moves from Sherman two or three times a week..

FOOT ROLL

1 Sit at your desk or on a couch and place a soup can (on its side) or a tennis ball on the floor in front of you.
2 Rest the arch of your injured foot (without shoes on) on the can or tennis ball and press down slightly while rolling the can up and down your foot, from your heel to your midarch.
3 Perform this for one minute, rest for 30 seconds, then repeat twice more.
WHY "This tackles the problem at the source by lengthening and softening the offending plantar fascia in order to release the pressure that's magnifying the heel pain," says Sherman.

TOE FLEXES

1 Sit with your injured leg straight out in front of you. Loop a towel around your foot, holding the ends with both hands.
2 Position your foot so that the towel goes around the arch, and pull the towel tight toward you.
3 Keeping your injured knee straight, push your foot away from your body and apply resistance with the towel. Do three sets of 10 repetitions.
WHY "You'll strengthen your calf muscles and Achilles tendon while the force from the towel against your plantar fascia stretches it out, to provide a two-pronged approach to fast recovery," says Sherman.

PLANTAR STRETCH

1 Cross your legs and put your right ankle (assuming this is your affected foot) above your left knee so the underside of your foot is facing you.
2 Grab your toes and pull them back.
3 Hold this position for 10 seconds, then release. Repeat 10 times. Do three to six times a day, starting when you get up in the morning.
WHY "This stretch isolates the plantar fascia, and after subjects did it for eight weeks, there was a dramatic improvement over those who only stretched their Achilles," says orthopedic surgeon Ben DiGiovanni.

HOW LONG UNTIL YOU'RE RECOVERED

Studies in the *American Family Physician* state that these are the expected recovery rates.

>> **MILD INJURY**
100% after 2-6 months

>> **AVERAGE INJURY**
100% after 9-12 months

>> **SEVERE INJURY**
100% after 18 months

NEVER GET HURT

It's a very simple exercise plan. And it may just help you run injury-free for the rest of your life

> **AT THE GYM, IT'S EASY TO SPOT** the runners. They're the ones with skinny legs and 3D quads who are doing squats, hamstring curls, and calf raises. There's only one problem: They're working the wrong muscles.

"Since the quads, hamstrings, and calves propel you forward, they're adequately strengthened through running," says Robert Wilder, M.D., medical director of the University of Virginia Center for Endurance Sports. "Other muscles, like your abs and glutes, aren't typically engaged when you run, but should be. They're the ones that need attention."

These underappreciated muscles provide the foundation for a strong pelvis. "Almost all common overuse injuries are related to a lack of pelvic stability," says Jay Dicharry, M.P.T., C.S.C.S., director of the University's Center for Endurance Sports.

Here's why. Picture a weak, wobbly pelvis. As you stride, one side rotates forward as the other drops down, forcing your back to overarch and your striding foot to rotate inward. Wilder says these events cause muscular imbalances and tightness, which can lead to iliotibial band syndrome (ITBS), shinsplints, lower-back pain, and other muscular issues. On the other hand, if your pelvis is stable, your legs spin beneath you like wheels, your energy is directed forward, and your stride is light, efficient, and biomechanically correct.

The good news: You can get there with targeted training. The following routine engages your transverse abdominals (the deep abs that stabilize the spine and pelvis) and your gluteus medius (the muscle on the side of your glutes that minimizes side-to-side rotation). The regimen begins with simple exercises that focus on abdominal bracing—pulling your belly button up and in—and get progressively harder. Be sure to do them in order and maintain braced abs as you progress.

Do this 20-minute routine at least three times a week before a run, so you reinforce the correct muscle engagement before you're in motion. The results you feel as you run (and run and run) will be dramatic.

CENTER OF ATTENTION
Work the right muscles to avoid injury.

IMAGES: BETH BISCHOFF

HEALTH AND INJURY

1 PRONE MARCH

WHY To imprint the feeling of braced abs and a stable pelvis, and to teach your muscles how to fire the deep core stabilizers before you engage your leg muscles.

HOW 1 Lie on your back with your hands on your hips, both knees bent at a 45-degree angle, and your feet flat on the floor. 2 With braced abs and lower back flat on the floor, lift your left leg until your calf is parallel to the floor, then return to the start. Repeat 15 times with each leg.

MAKE IT HARDER As you get stronger, lift both legs at once, then alternate lowering each leg.

2 PRONE DRIVE

WHY To lengthen your hip flexors without moving your pelvis.

HOW 1 Lie flat on your back with braced abs and a neutral spine, and lift both feet off the floor so your knees are bent at 90 degrees and your calves are parallel to the floor. Then, keeping one leg stable, extend your other leg forward as though you were driving off it during a run. 2 Tap your heel on the ground for an instant, then return to the start. Alternate legs for 15 reps on each side.

MAKE IT HARDER Maintain your form and gradually increase the speed of your drives.

3 SIDE LIFT

WHY To promote a stable pelvis as the gluteus muscles engage and the hip flexors extend. This can help prevent pain in your knees and your IT band (tissue down your thigh). **HOW 1** Lie on your right side, hips in line with your shoulders, right knee bent 60 degrees, left hand on left hip, head on right arm.

2 Flex your left foot and raise your left leg, toes angled slightly off the ground, a few inches off the floor. With a stable pelvis—use your left hand to check that it isn't moving—lift your left leg back and rotate it slightly (no more than 45 degrees) toward the ceiling. Repeat 15 times on each side.

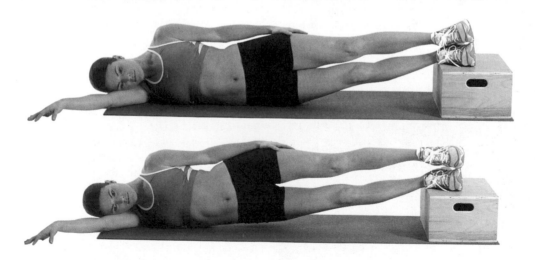

4 INVERTED BRIDGE

WHY To engage your deep core muscles and strengthen the gluteus medius, reinforcing correct muscle-firing pattern. **HOW 1** Lie on your right side, with your head resting on your right arm and your left arm extended along your left side. Stack

both feet on a block that is between eight and 14 inches high. 2 Brace your abs. Keeping your hips in line with your shoulders, press your right leg into the block as you raise your pelvis off the floor. Pause, then lower. Aim for 30 reps on each side.

5 HIP HIKE

WHY To mimic proper gluteus function during touchdown while running, strengthen hip mechanics, and improve balance.

HOW 1 Stand on a step or box with your right foot on the edge and your left foot off it, arms by your sides, abs braced. Keeping your right knee bent slightly, lower the left side of your pelvis so that your left foot drops a few inches below your right. 2 Then hike your pelvis up so that the left foot is above your right foot. Lift and lower for 30 reps on each side. **MAKE IT HARDER** Do this movement before—and during—your runs by finding a curb. It helps remind you how your glutes should feel.

6 DRIVE THROUGH

WHY To teach optimal alignment and engagement for the propulsion stage of running, and to target all lower-body muscles and improve balance.

HOW 1 Stand on your left foot, arms at sides, abs braced. Keeping your back flat and your weight over the ball of your left foot, assume a position as if you were running—bend your left knee and extend your right leg behind you, knee bent 90 degrees, your right arm bent in front of you. 2 In one smooth motion, drive your right knee and left arm forward as you come up on the ball of your left foot. Pause, then repeat. Do 30 reps on each side.

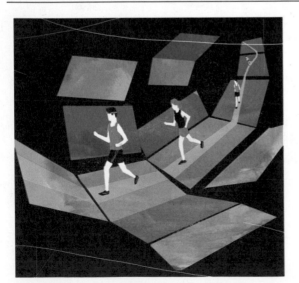

ROADSIDE ASSISTANCE
HOW TO PREVENT INJURIES WHILE YOU RUN

The plan detailed here can help you become injury-free, especially if you apply it while you run. "Concentrate on your form until it becomes habit," says Dicharry. To help you, he offers the following tips:

MECHANICAL MUSTS

›As you run, check that your transverse abdominals, the muscles that stabilize the spine and pelvis, are engaged by putting your fingers lightly above your pelvic bones. The muscles should feel tight.
›A thunderous heel-strike will often presage an aching back. "You could be overstriding, which makes you overarch your lower back," he says. Instead, try to maintain a long, neutral spine. To do that, stop running and locate proper posture: Put one

7 UPPER STAR

WHY To develop stability, strength, and balance in each leg.
HOW 1 Lay five objects in a semicircle in front of you (on a clock, they'd be at 9, 10:30, 12, 1:30, and 3). Stand two feet behind the 12 on your right foot, left calf bent 90 degrees behind you. Place your right hand on your hip.

2 Bend forward from the hips, so that your right knee is over your toes. Reach out with your left arm toward the 9–don't reach down, but to the side so your hand is over it–then return to upright. Reach toward 10:30, then return to standing. Repeat until you get to 3. Then start with your right arm at 3 and work toward 9. Switch legs, and repeat.

8 LOWER STAR

WHY Develops stability, strength, and balance.
HOW 1 This time, line up the five objects in a semicircle on one side of you (on a clock, they'd be positioned at 6, 7:30, 9, 10:30, and 12). Stand about two feet across from the 9 object, balancing on your right foot. Keeping your hands on your hips and

your back straight, brace your abs. Bend your right knee so it is lined up over your toes. Then reach back with your left foot toward 6. Without touching your toe to the floor, stand back up.
2 Aim for 7:30, then return to standing. Repeat until you get to 12, then go back to 6. Turn around and repeat on the opposite leg.

hand on your belly button and the other on your breastbone, then lengthen your spine and engage your transverse abs to shorten the distance between your hands.

> A heavy heel-strike also wreaks havoc on your muscles. Land with your foot directly underneath you to control your balance and stability.

> Next time you huff up a hill, note your form: You probably had a natural forward lean, centered each footstrike underneath your body, and took small, rapid steps. Try to mimic this form on all kinds of terrain.

> While running downhill, lean forward like a skier so your body stays perpendicular to the hill. This prevents a damaging heel-strike.

> When you hit a gentle downhill, focus on your transverse abs and your posture to keep strides short.

3 GOLDEN RULES

>>THE LONGEST RUN OF THE WEEK Should never be more than half of your weekly total. So if you're running 20 miles a week, your longest run is 10 miles, maximum.

>>NO LIMPING Limping means you're compromising your form, and you'll eventually pay the price. If you feel minor pain–below 3 on a scale

of 1 to 10, keep running. If the discomfort rises above 3, stop.

>>INCREASE MILEAGE No more than 10 percent weekly. Push too hard too fast, and you'll get hurt. "There are exceptions," says Dicharry. "If you ran 80 miles but dropped to 20 to heal an injury, you can step up more quickly."

GAIN FROM PAIN

Injuries happen to all but the very luckiest of runners, so here's how to be best prepared if discomfort comes your way

> **IF YOU DO DEVELOP AN INJURY**—and if you run for long enough, you likely will—it can be a miserable experience. It's easy to become bogged down in a gloom at the injustice of it all. Which, of course, does you no good—just the opposite, in fact. Recovery is your goal, and what you need is an effective way to bridge that depressing gap between the day you're forced to stop running and the day you can start again.

It's up to you. You can wallow in self-pity, lose your aerobic base, put on weight, and make yourself and everyone around you miserable—or you can keep in shape so you're ready to go as soon as the ache clears. Here's the plan:

1 NO WHINING

Keep your running injuries in perspective. Most are relatively minor and will heal in due time. It may seem catastrophic when you can't run, but don't moan—no one wants to hear it. Not your partner, not your children, not even your running friends. Besides, complaining is counterproductive to regaining your health and fitness.
THE GAIN You'll stay positive during the layoff, thus speeding your recovery.

2 BE PATIENT

There are very few runners who haven't been injured at one time or another, and the vast majority of those runners—even one 72-year-old who broke his hip—was able to run again. Unfortunately, no magic pill will cure you instantly. Instead, be confident that regardless of how bad your injury may seem, it's only temporary. You will run again, if you're patient enough.
THE GAIN You'll give your injury time to heal.

3 EAT PROPERLY

When you're running, it's easy to go on a "see-food" diet. Any food you see, you eat—in large quantities. So when you stop running, it's easy to stack on the pounds unless you exercise a little dietary control. It doesn't mean going on a crash diet; reduced nutrition lessens the body's ability to repair itself. But by focusing on low-fat goodies, fruit, and veggies, rather than beer and chips, you can assist your body's healing process and avoid adding pounds. When you resume running, any weight gain will come off quickly.
THE GAIN Staying lean will keep self-confidence up.

4 IF YOU HAVE A ROUTINE, STICK TO IT

That is, if you normally run at lunchtime, continue with some sort of exercise at lunchtime. If you're an early morning runner, go for a walk early in the morning.

Try walking one of your favorite routes, maybe a trail, and take the time to enjoy the landscape. A two-hour walk followed by typical postrun rituals will deliver recuperation benefits while keeping your morale at healthy levels.
THE GAIN By sticking with some semblance of exercise ritual, you'll reap many of its mood-boosting benefits.

5 DO IT OUTDOORS

Fresh air is never better than when you're injured. You can scoop up a lot of it on a bike ride. Processing lungfuls of oxygen is one of the things that make you feel good when running, and you'll achieve a similar effect by doing just about any outdoor activity.
THE GAIN Checking out the world around you will

take your mind off your injury, and you'll be
revitalized by a daily dose of fresh air, scenery, and
(hopefully) sunlight.

6 STAY CONNECTED

One of the worst aspects of being injured is not being
able to run with friends. The only time you may see
some of them is when you run together. So when
you're out of action, make an effort to stay in touch
and at least feel like you're part of the running scene.
One way to do this is to volunteer to help at races.
Take the opportunity to spend more time with your
family and nonrunning friends; you've got no excuse
for dropping out of things such as playing football
with the kids or going to a late-night party.
THE GAIN Instead of becoming too self-absorbed,
you'll keep lines of communication open with your
friends, family, and the running community.

7 SWEAT

If you normally run 45 minutes a day, make sure you
do some activity vigorous enough to keep you aerobic
for 45 minutes. It doesn't matter too much what you
do, as long as it doesn't aggravate the existing injury.
Hit the exercise bike or use some sort of indoor
trainer: a cross-country ski machine, a treadmill, or a
stair-climber. More importantly, several studies
suggest that if you do these alternatives with enough
intensity, they can maintain and even increase your
fitness level.
THE GAIN You'll end up with a puddle of sweat and a
soggy T-shirt—evidence you've done something to
burn calories and retain your aerobic base.

8 LIFT WEIGHTS

Since you're going to be at the gym anyway, riding a
stationary bike or on the elliptical, it's not
a big deal to spend another 20 minutes with weights.
Aim to do legwork, along with some core and
upper-body moves. Just talk with your doctor to
make sure you don't worsen your injury.
THE GAIN You'll burn calories and maintain overall
fitness and muscle tone.

9 MAKE A DAILY EFFORT

While injuries can be markedly different,
most of them respond extremely well to rest and
self-treatment. If there are things you can do—see
a chiropractor or podiatrist, have a massage—do
them. If all you need to do is ice the injury or take
anti-inflammatories, do it religiously. If muscle
inflexibility or imbalance may have contributed

to the problem, stretch carefully twice a day.
THE GAIN By taking action, you'll speed recovery
and achieve peace of mind.

10 FOCUS ON TODAY

Don't set an arbitrary deadline for when you'll be
ready and then start, whether you're healthy or not.
With any luck, you'll only be out of action for
a few weeks at the most, but you never know how
quickly you'll heal. It doesn't follow that an injury
that took four days to heal last time will do so again.
As you age, it takes longer for your body to heal.
THE GAIN By not setting strict deadlines, you
won't become frustrated when you miss them.
More important, you won't start running before
you're ready.

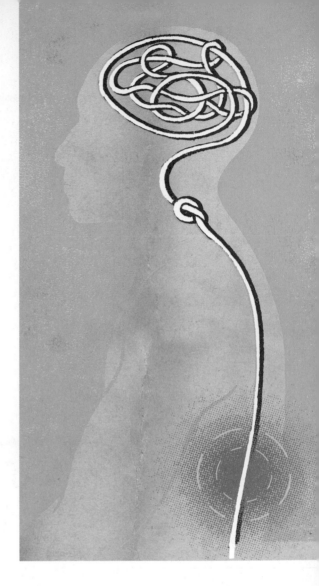

ILLUSTRATION: EDEL RODRIGUEZ

HEALTH AND INJURY

WHERE IT HURTS

Nine ways a runner can feel the burn—and then deal with it.

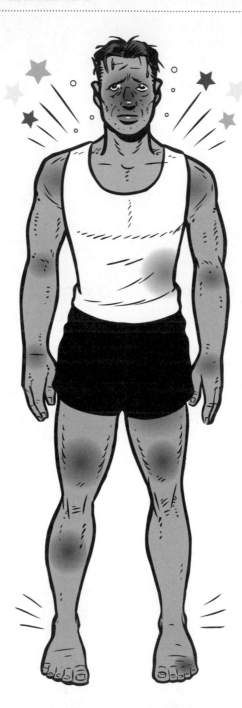

>>**DEHYDRATION**
OUCH You're parched and your heart races.
SCIENCE Plain and simple: You've lost too much fluid.
CURE Drink! Water is best to quench the thirst, but drink what you crave.

>>**HITTING THE RED ZONE**
OUCH Your muscles burn—everything's on fire.
SCIENCE Many call this "going anaerobic," but there's little evidence that the pain arises from too little oxygen (or too much lactic acid). Rather, your brain recognizes you're too close to your limit and forces you to slow down.
CURE Ease up soon—or it's game over.

>>**LEG CRAMPS**
OUCH Your muscles are seizing up big time.
SCIENCE Electrical impulses in the muscles have gone haywire, causing rapid contractions.
CURE Stop and stretch.

>>**SHINSPLINTS**
OUCH Your shins are sore.
SCIENCE Pain is likely due to overtraining, wearing worn shoes, or uneven surfaces.
CURE Walk it out. Avoid relapses by doing stretching and strengthening exercises.

>>**HITTING THE WALL**
OUCH You're out of energy.
SCIENCE You've depleted your liver's supply of glycogen, and it can't maintain blood glucose.

CURE Begin long runs with full glycogen stores and down carbs when runs top 75 minutes. Aim for one to two ounces per hour.

<<**SIDE STITCH**
OUCH A stabbing pain pierces your side.
SCIENCE Theories abound. The most popular: cramp in your diaphragm muscle.
CURE Focus on breathing with your diaphragm by pulling your stomach in as you exhale and pushing out as you inhale.

<<**CHAFING**
OUCH Tender skin feels like it's burning.
SCIENCE Friction between skin and skin (or skin and clothing) rubs you raw.
CURE Avoid clothing with stitching in chafe-prone areas, and apply lube to potential hot spots.

<<**LEG LOCK**
OUCH Your muscles feel like they're filled with cement.
SCIENCE You've run in the red zone too long and damaged muscle fibers. Your brain is slowing down your muscles to protect you.
CURE The damage is done—just slow down.

<<**BLISTERS**
OUCH A skin bubble on your foot burns.
SCIENCE Friction rubs skin raw. Moisture makes it worse.
CURE Try preventive taping, or lube problem areas and keep feet dry. Wear socks of moisture-wicking material, or thin, double-layer socks.

There's a coach in every watch.

Meet the GPS running watches with coaching features so dialed-in, they might know your abilities better than you do. 220 gives you essential running data like distance, pace and heart rate. The 620 adds a touchscreen, VO2 max estimating and a recovery advisor. And when you pair 620 with HRM-Run you have access to advanced running form coaching data like cadence, vertical oscillation and ground contact time. Both 220 and 620 are compatible with free training plans from Garmin Connect™, which you can send to your watch, for real-time coaching.

To learn more, visit Garmin.com/ForerunnerCoach

GARMIN.

©2014 Garmin Ltd. or its subsidiaries

Forerunner® 220 | 620

CENTER OF ATTENTION

Forget crunches. If you want to get faster, fitter, and stronger, you need to train your core like a runner

IN THE PAST you'd have been hard-pressed to find elite runners paying attention to their abs. Today, it's mandatory. "It's so important. The stronger the core, the more likely you are to hold your form and less likely to get injured," explains marathon world record holder Paula Radcliffe. You simply can't run your best without a strong core: the muscles in your abdominals, lower back, and glutes. They provide the stability, power, and endurance that runners need for powering up hills, sprinting to the finish, and maintaining form mile after mile. "When your core is strong, everything else will follow," says running coach Greg McMillan, who has worked with scores of elite and recreational runners. "It's the foundation for all of your movement, no matter what level of running you're doing."

The key is to train your core like a specialist. Quality core work isn't easy, but it doesn't require much of your time, says running coach Nick Anderson. "You don't need to put in more than 15 minutes a few times a week." It's an investment that will pay dividends on the road.

KNOW YOUR CORE

A close look at the muscle groups that make up your core

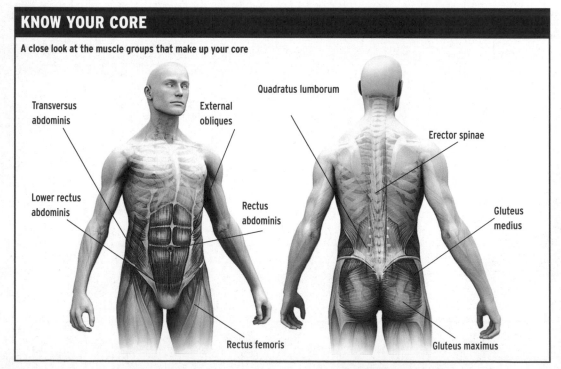

Transversus abdominis

External obliques

Quadratus lumborum

Erector spinae

Lower rectus abdominis

Rectus abdominis

Gluteus medius

Rectus femoris

Gluteus maximus

IMAGE: JOSHUA SIMPSON; ILLUSTRATIONS: SUPERCORN, JOHN McNEIL

CROSS-TRAINING

THE STRONGER THE CORE, THE LESS LIKELY YOU ARE TO GET INJURED.

HOW YOUR CORE WORKS ON THE ROAD

A strong midsection will help you maintain form, avoid injury, and finish races faster. This is why.

SPEED

As you extend your stride or quicken the rate of your leg and foot turnover when you're trying to pick up the pace, the lower abs—including the transversus and rectus abdominis—and lower back are called into action. The stronger and more stable these muscles are, the more force and speed you can generate as you push off the ground.

UPHILLS

The glutes and lower abs support the pelvis, which connects to the leg muscles needed to get uphill. If the core is strong, the legs have a stable plane to push from, for a more powerful ascent. When you swing your leg forward, the rectus femoris muscles pull on the pelvis. As you push off the ground, the glutes and hamstrings are engaged.

DOWNHILLS

When you're flying down a slope, you need strong gluteal muscles to help absorb the impact and counter the momentum of the forward motion. As fun as it may be to zoom down, without the core strength to control your movement, your quads and knee joints bear the extra pounding of your body weight, which can lead to fatigue, pain, and injury.

ENDURANCE

As you near the end of a race, a solid core helps you maintain proper form and run efficiently, even through fatigue. With strong lower abs and lower-back muscles, such as the erector spinae, it's easier to stay upright. If your core is weak, you may end up shuffling, slouching, and putting too much stress on your hips, knees, and shins.

LATERAL MOVEMENT

Whenever you have to suddenly move to the side—to turn the corner on a track, dodge a pothole, or navigate undulating terrain—the obliques provide stability and help keep you upright. If your core is weak, then you may end up leaning into the movement, which can put excess weight and strain on the joints in your legs and feet.

IMAGE: JOSÉ MANDOJANA

BEYOND CRUNCHES

THE 15-MINUTE WORKOUT DESIGNED JUST FOR RUNNERS

Fortunately, quality core strength work doesn't require a great deal of time or equipment—just 15 minutes three times a week, a few feet of floor space, and some key moves done correctly and consistently. This workout is designed by Greg McMillan, a running coach and exercise scientist who has worked with many recreational runners and world-class athletes. The workout is devised to strengthen the specific muscles runners need for bounding up hills, sprinting to the finish, enduring long distances, and preventing common running injuries. Try doing two sets of these moves right before or after your run, three times a week.

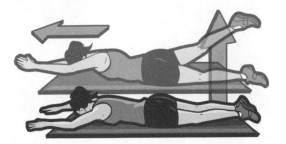

SUPERMAN

WHAT IT HITS Transversus abdominis (deep abs) and erector spinae (lower back)

HOW Start face down on the floor, with your arms and legs extended out in front. Raise your head, your left arm, and right leg five inches off the floor. Hold for three counts, then lower. Repeat with your right arm and left leg. Do up to 10 reps on each side.

GET IT RIGHT Don't raise your shoulders too much.

MAKE IT HARDER Lift both arms and legs at the same time.

BRIDGE

WHAT IT HITS Glutes and hamstrings

HOW Lie face up on the floor, with your knees bent 90 degrees, your feet on the floor. Lift your hips and back off the floor until your body forms a straight line from your shoulders to your knees. Hold for five to 10 seconds. Lower to the floor and repeat 10 to 12 times.

GET IT RIGHT Squeeze your glutes at the top of the movement, and don't let your spine sag.

MAKE IT HARDER Straighten one leg once your hips are lifted.

METRONOME

WHAT IT HITS Obliques

HOW Lie face up with your knees bent and raised over your hips, with your shins parallel to the ground, your feet lifted, and your arms out. Rotate your legs to the left, bringing your knees as close to the floor as possible without touching. Return to the center, then rotate your knees to the right. Do 10 to 12 reps on each side.

GET IT RIGHT Make sure not to swing your hips or use momentum; start the movement from your core and continue to move slowly from side to side.

MAKE IT HARDER Keep your legs straight.

BIRD DOG
Improves core strength and balance.

ALL THE RIGHT MOVES A few quick fixes will pay off on the run

THE MISTAKE
YOU'RE DOING THE WRONG EXERCISES
"The biggest mistake that runners tend to make is to take strength-training moves, such as crunches, straight from the fitness industry," says running coach Greg McMillan. For most runners, standard crunches aren't helpful because they don't work the deep core muscles that provide the stability to run mile after mile.
THE FIX
Do workouts that hit the muscles and movements that runners need. Try exercises like the side plank or plank lift (opposite) that strengthen the obliques, on the sides of the trunk, and the transverse abs, the deep core muscles that wrap around the trunk like a corset. These muscles stabilize the core, help counter rotation, and minimize wasteful movement so that you run more efficiently.

THE MISTAKE
YOU'RE A CREATURE OF HABIT
Even if you've moved beyond crunches, you may find you have slipped into a routine. "You need to constantly challenge your muscles to get results," says running coach Sam Murphy.
THE FIX
Mix it up. Fine-tune your workout to make it more difficult. Try balancing on one leg or changing your arm position. At the gym, use devices like a stability ball—an unstable platform that forces your core muscles to work harder to keep you steady.

And as a rule, McMillan says, change your routine around every six weeks or so.

THE MISTAKE
YOU WHIP THROUGH YOUR WORKOUTS
If you're flying through the moves in your workout, you're using momentum, not muscles.
THE FIX
Slow it down. Exercises like the plank, which require holding one position for 10 to 60 seconds, force you to work your muscles continuously. Even in exercises that involve repetitions, make steady—not rapid-fire—movements. "It takes intention," says Paula Coates, running coach, physiotherapist, and author of *Running Repairs: A Runner's Guide to Keeping Injury Free.*

"Don't rush through them, and make sure you're doing them properly."

THE MISTAKE
YOU IGNORE WHAT YOU DON'T SEE
Runners often have weak backs because they just forget about them, says running coach Nick Anderson. "But when you're running, especially if you're running for a long time, those muscles in the lower back are crucial for providing stability and support."
THE FIX
Include at least one exercise that hits the lower back and glutes in each workout. Moves like the bridge and superman (previous page) build muscles that support and protect the spine.

IMAGES: JOSHUA SIMPSON

PREVENTIVE ACTION Prehab problem areas to run injury-free

Your core is like a power plant. If it's not working efficiently, you'll waste energy, says Tim Hilden, a physical therapist, coach, and physiologist who specializes in running. "You'll see too much unwanted movement, which decreases performance or sets you up for injury." Here are three areas that can be injured as a result of a weak core.

>>LOWER BACK
As your legs pound the pavement, your vertebrae absorb much of the force. That shock worsens if your core is weak, which will produce lower-back pain. Build those muscles with moves like the superman (previous spread).
>>HAMSTRINGS
When your core isn't stable, your hamstrings often have to work extra hard, says running coach and physiotherapist Paula Coates. The added work can leave them shorter, tighter, and more vulnerable to injury. To strengthen them, as well as your glutes, try exercises like bridges, lunges, and squats.
>>KNEES
Without a stable core, you can't control the movement of your torso as well, and you risk putting excess force on your joints each time your foot lands. This can lead to pain under the knee (known as "runner's knee"), patellar tendinitis (a sharp pain in the bottom of the knee), and iliotibial-band tendinitis. The plank (below left) strengthens the transversus abdominis, which help steady the core.

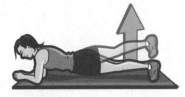

SIDE PLANK
WHAT IT HITS Obliques, transversus abdominis, lower back, hips, and glutes
HOW Lie on your right side, supporting your upper body on your right forearm, with your left arm at your side. Lift your hips and, keeping your body weight supported on the forearm and the side of the right foot, extend your left arm above your shoulder. Hold for 10 to 30 seconds. Switch sides and repeat.
GET IT RIGHT Keep your hips up; don't let them sag.
MAKE IT HARDER Support your upper body with your right hand, not your forearm.

PLANK LIFT
WHAT IT HITS Transversus abdominis and lower back
HOW Begin face down on the floor, propped up on your forearms, with knees and feet together. With your elbows under your shoulders, lift your torso, legs, and hips in a straight line. Hold for 10 seconds. Raise your right leg a few inches, keeping the rest of the body still. Lower and repeat with your left leg.
GET IT RIGHT Pull in your belly and don't let your hips sag.
MAKE IT HARDER Extend the time of the exercise.

PLANK
Hold for 30 to 60 seconds to work the core.

BALANCING ACTS

Try these alternative approaches to ensure you have a long and satisfying running life

YOGA

In the early to mid-1990s, Uta Pippig was one of the best marathon runners in the world, winning Boston three times in a row. But by 2000, things had changed. "I was stuck in a rut, exhausted, and mentally tired," she says. Her savior? Yoga. "It helped me regain my energy, improve my breathing, and find inner peace and satisfaction."

Yoga has been credited with everything from helping people reach a higher spiritual sphere to creating Madonna's muscles (nothing to do with running and resistance work, then?). Meanwhile, runners and their coaches are divided about how much difference it will make to your performance, but as people like Pippig will testify, it offers mental space and a good stretch—which can't do any harm.

"Yoga teaches you to be in an intense situation—perhaps deep in a back-bending pose—and to bring awareness to your form and your breathing to make the situation manageable," says yoga instructor and triathalon coach Sage Rountree. "This skill is invaluable at mile 18 of a marathon. You'll learn ways to cope that benefit you as an athlete and in life."

There are dozens of types of yoga. Treat intense classes (Ashtanga or power yoga) as hard sessions and fit them into your training accordingly. Classes in Hatha yoga are very popular and should offer a more gentle stretch. It's best to start with an instructor, but Rountree recommends developing a home-based practice that you can adjust to your running schedule: poses that stretch your muscles postrun; others that strengthen your core three times a week; and a longer routine that works the whole body on a rest day.

TRY THIS

PYRAMID
WHY Promotes stability, stretches hamstrings
HOW Stand tall and relaxed with your right leg in front of you. Hinge forward from the hips, tilting the pelvis forward and keeping the back straight, with your knee slightly bent. Interlace your fingers behind your back and stretch them up and away from you. Repeat on the other side.

REVERSE TABLE
WHY Strengthens your abs and back
HOW Sit with your knees bent, feet on the floor, hands directly under your shoulders with your fingers spread. Push up through your hands and feet until your torso and thighs are parallel to the floor.

LUNGE WITH TWIST
WHY Stretches the hips
HOW Step your left foot back; lower down so your knee and toes rest on the ground and your front knee is just beyond a right angle. Put your palms together and keep your shoulders down. Twist from the waist and rest your left triceps on your right quad. Look over your shoulder. Repeat on the other side.

IMAGES: MITCH MANDEL; STUDIO 33, JOHN HICKS

CROSS-TRAINING

PILATES

Workouts that strengthen your core are popular these days, but the idea of strengthening your back, abdominals, and pelvic muscles to benefit your whole body isn't new. Joseph Pilates called the core the "powerhouse." Pilates was a German-born sportsman and fitness trainer, who began developing his method while training other inmates in a prisoner-of-war camp during World War I. Afterward, he moved to New York, where, with his wife, he set up his first studio, teaching "Contrology," the system now known as Pilates.

Runners are often advised to take up Pilates to prevent injury, but you'll need patience because Pilates is meant to be performed slowly.

There are different approaches to Pilates, but all of them can benefit runners. It can be performed using special equipment, or on a mat. Your pelvic floor should be contracted throughout, but not strongly. Breathe "laterally" into the sides of your chest (use a mirror to watch your chest expanding, or have a partner check with their hands on your ribs), so you can hold your tummy in through the exercises. Perform movements during the exhalation.

TRY THIS

PLANK AND V

WHY Works core, stretches calves, hamstrings, and back
HOW 1 Start in a plank—face down in a press-up position, supported by your forearms and toes. Your back should be straight, tummy in, and pelvic floor lightly contracted.
2 Push your hips and bottom up and let your heels drop so you're in an inverted V position. Return to the plank. Repeat 10 times, slowly, without resting.

REVERSE CRUNCH AND V

WHY Works core and back
HOW 1 Start on your back with arms by your side. Use abs to pull hips up and legs over your head. Move your legs apart, then together.
2 Roll down and up into an upright V position. As you come up, bring your arms up and lightly hold the outside of your legs to help you balance. In the V position, move your legs apart and together again, roll back down to the floor, and start the movement again. Repeat 10 times.

SIDE KICKS AND FIGURE EIGHT

WHY Works the core, glutes, and outer thigh muscles
HOW 1 Lie on your side with a rolled towel between your head and bottom arm for support. Contract your abs and lift both legs slightly. Move one leg forward and one leg back, then switch.

2 When you've completed 10, keep your legs off the floor and raise your upper leg slightly. Point your toes and draw a sideways figure eight, keeping your upper body still. Build up to 10. Repeat on the other side.

ALEXANDER TECHNIQUE

You may have heard that it's best to "run tall," but few of us know what it means. You can force it, but you'll probably stick your chest out. A trained teacher in the Alexander Technique can help you find the position that frees up your legs and arms.

Frederick Alexander was an Australian performer who specialized in monologues, but he suffered from hoarseness. He noticed that he tensed up when performing, and set about letting go of the habits that were affecting his voice. The result, now known as Alexander Technique (AT), is used to help everyone from musicians to athletes. AT teacher and athlete Malcolm Balk has applied it to running, with an approach to the sport that uses elements of the Pose and Chi running methods but centers on the principles of AT, including the relationship between the head, neck, and spine.

You'll need patience and hands-on guidance to follow this approach, so you should forget about times while you're learning. One of the main principles is avoiding "end-gaining"—you think, "I'm going to run 20 minutes for 5-K, and if I don't, I'll feel terrible." Which is nonsense—don't set yourself up for failure.

TRY THIS... AN RW EDITOR DID!

THE ART OF RUNNING WORKSHOP

Bad running techniques are picked up over years, so you might wonder how much you can learn about running well in three hours. The answer is: a lot. I've been running for nine years but snatch PRs between bouts of injury. I spend my day slouched over a desk and carry my bad habits with me on every run, so I was interested to find out what Malcolm Balk and Liz Dodgson, both AT experts, would make of my gait.

Video analysis showed that I used an up-and-down, heel-striking gait. Balk explained the problems with this: Striking in front of the body causes braking, while the exaggerated push off the ground wastes energy.

The rest of the workshop was aimed at relearning how to run, beginning with some AT basics: Balk and Dodgson helped me find a comfortable, aligned position lying down. Moving outside, we paired up to support each other's necks, to give an awareness of walking with a long spine and balanced head. We ran through some drills designed to encourage a more efficient running action: swinging each leg to engage the hamstrings and glutes; lightly pawing the ground to learn the "wheel-like" action of the correct gait; and lightly bouncing then jogging on the spot on the midfoot. Then it was time to put this together into a new, momentum-aided run.

Few of us got it right the first time. Physically, it was easier than I expected but mentally it felt strange. "If it doesn't feel weird, something's wrong," said Balk. "That would mean you're slipping back into your old habits."

So, no one came away with a set, super-efficient stride, but a second video analysis showed improvements. Balk himself admitted he still has to think about running well every time he goes out. What the workshop gave me was the tools to give my own running that consideration, instead of pounding out step after injury-inducing step.

Find out more at theartofrunning.com.

GET THE PICTURE
Balk holds up his own style for analysis.

STRETCHING OUT
To help find the right gait

STARTING POINT
The importance of proper alignment

A HELPING HAND
Learning how to walk tall

BAND AID

Running's your thing. Pumping iron isn't. But strength training can toughen you up, so we've come up with a solution: a fast, simple routine that'll improve your running—no iron required

> **STRENGTH TRAINING IS A BIT LIKE FLOSSING:** We know it's good for us, but we don't do it as often as we should. Successful runners do more than just run—they lift and lunge to build strong muscles for climbing hills, maintaining perfect form, and preventing injuries. But it can be hard to run well when you're recovering from a weights workout. Plus, squeezing running into your schedule can be tough enough as it is. And you probably don't want to join a gym; after all, one of the reasons you're a runner is that you can do it wherever you are.

Well, enough excuses: Tom Sheehan, director of strength and conditioning at Columbia University, has designed a resistance-band program for runners that provides all the benefits of lifting weights with none of the hassles. The bands put constant tension on the body, and they produce a challenging cardiovascular workout. Also, the resistance provided by the bands doesn't overload joints like a dumbbell can. As a result, there's less risk of injury, more work that can be performed in a single session, and faster recovery between workouts.

"Your knees, shoulders, and back won't hurt the next day," says Sheehan, "so there's minimal impact on your running." Several of the exercises in the band program require multiple muscles to work simultaneously to perform a single move. "The bands work on synchronizing the lower and upper body, which helps provide core stability, balance, and muscular power—all things that can improve a runner's performance," says Sheehan.

GETTING STARTED

Here's how you can jump on the bandwagon: Get hold of some bands and a bench. Two or three times a week, put in your miles first, and then do one of the workouts below, alternating between them. Each takes 20 to 30 minutes. Except where noted, do three sets of 20 reps. Increase the reps each week until you get to 50, then increase the resistance.

FULL-BODY WORKOUT OPTIONS

WORKOUT 1
- ›› Overhead press and squat
- ›› Two-leg squat
- ›› Overhead tricep extension
- ›› Abs/lower-back extension
- ›› Bench press

WORKOUT 2
- ›› Overhead press and back lunge
- ›› Single-leg squat
- ›› One-arm row
- ›› Shoulder press
- ›› Overhead tricep extension
- ›› Abs/lower-back extension

IMAGES: ERIN PATRICE O'BRIEN

OVERHEAD PRESS AND SQUAT

1 Attach two bands to the handles, then stand on the bottom band with both feet. Holding the top band, press your arms up and out to a 45-degree angle so your body looks like a "Y."

2 Bend your knees and squat until your thighs are parallel with the floor—go lower if you can. Return to standing, then lower your arms to your shoulders. Repeat.

CROSS-TRAINING

BENCH PRESS

1 Wrap the band around the back leg of the bench. Lie back on the bench with your feet flat on it. Hold the handles with your elbows bent and your hands in line with your chest.

2 Press your arms straight up until your hands are over midchest. Lower and repeat.

TWO-LEG SQUAT

1 Secure the band underneath the bench. Holding the handles, stand on the bench with your arms straight down at your sides. Feet should be shoulder-width apart, chest over midfoot, hips back, knees behind toes.

2 Bending at the knee and hip, lower yourself down for a three-second count until you get to a quarter-squat position. Pause for a moment, then, pushing through your midfoot, drive upward to full extension. This three-seconds down, pause, up-fast should be one continuous movement. Repeat.

OVERHEAD TRICEP EXTENSION

1 Using two bands attached to the handles, stand on the lower band with your right foot and pull the upper band up behind your head so your elbows are bent at 90 degrees. Your elbows should be near your ears.

2 Maintaining tension on the band, press your arms overhead by extending at the elbows only. Return to the starting position and repeat.

ABS/LOWER-BACK EXTENSION

1 Lie flat on your back with the band under the bottom of your feet. Grab the band under the handles and hold it at your hips with your arms fully extended on the floor.

2 Keeping your arms and legs straight, jackknife your arms and legs up until the body is in a "V" position with just your upper buttocks on the floor. Push back down to full, flat extension on the floor. (Note: A more resistant band places emphasis on the lower back; a lighter band makes the abs work harder.) Do two sets of 30 to 50 reps.

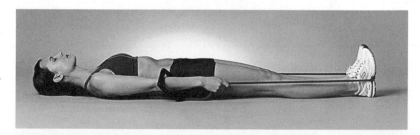

CROSS-TRAINING

ONE-ARM ROW

1 Secure the middle part of the band under the front leg of the bench. With your left foot on the floor and your right knee on the bench, hold the handle in your left hand. Your right palm should be flat on the bench under your

right shoulder and your back should be straight.

2 Leading the move with your elbow, pull the handle into your waist. Lower and repeat, doing all reps on the left side, then switch sides and do the same on the right side.

OVERHEAD PRESS AND BACK LUNGE

1 Attach two bands to the handles, then stand on the lower band with your left foot while holding the upper band at a 45-degree angle so your body looks like a "Y."

2 Maintaining tension on the bands, step your right foot back two to three feet and drop your right knee down until it almost

touches the floor and your left thigh becomes parallel with the floor. Keep your weight on your front foot—your back leg is for balance only. Pushing up through the front foot, return your feet to the start position, and lower arms to shoulders. Do 20 reps lunging back with right foot, then switch sides.

SHOULDER PRESS

1 Sit on the bench with the band secured under the front leg. Hold the handle in your right hand and bend your right elbow 90 degrees so your hand is facing forward at eye level.

2 Press your arm straight up so your bicep is close to your right ear. Lower and repeat. Then do another complete set on the opposite side.

SINGLE-LEG SQUAT

1 Secure the band underneath the bench and stand with your left foot on it, holding the handle in your left hand. Your right leg should be straight and hanging off the bench, even with your left leg.

2 Push your hips back and down just as in the two-leg squat (see page 122), into the quarter-squat position. Push through your left foot to full extension. Repeat.

FAREWELL, FAT

Run faster, eat better, and lose 10 pounds in the next month

> **YOU'RE EITHER A RUNNER** or you want to be one. And you would like to be in good shape. But even if you are not clinically obese, that doesn't mean you're entirely satisfied with your current weight and that you're not interested in losing a few pounds in order to become healthier, feel better, and run stronger.

To demonstrate how easy that could be, we've set out a plan. The goal: Lose 10 pounds this month. The modus operandi: Run a series of fat-burning workouts each week; then watch what and how much you eat.

Now let's look at the numbers. To lose a pound, you have to burn roughly 3,500 calories. Ten pounds a month is 2.5 pounds a week. So you need to create an 8,750-calorie deficit each week—or 1,250 calories a day.

Wait! Before you throw up your hands in despair over these impossible-sounding targets (and reach for the Häagen-Dazs for comfort), remember that daily calorie input and output is a big numbers game.

Your body burns thousands of calories each day just sitting around. For instance, a 170-pound man burns 1,850 calories a day at rest and another 1,600 through normal daily activity. That's a total of 3,450 calories per day. Then, if he runs 30 minutes at seven-minute mile pace he burns another 540, which brings the total up to 3,990 a day. If he follows the weight-loss guidelines in this chapter to create a 1,250-calorie deficit each day, he can still consume 2,740 calories. All these principles apply to women, too, but on a smaller scale. Because women weigh less and have slower metabolisms, they burn fewer calories than men over the same activity. Now that the numbers aren't so daunting, let's take a closer look at how to lose those pounds.

RUNNING STRATEGIES THAT BURN CALORIES

Running is the most efficient way to shed weight. For our 170-pound man, running 30 minutes at a 10-minute mile pace will burn about 385 calories. Of course, there's the time-proven long run, which puts the body in the fat-burning zone, but these days, the shift is toward faster sessions, which burn calories and fat much more efficiently. A study at the University of Texas showed that fast running burns 33 percent more fat per minute than slower running. That can be a big help when you're trying to lose weight and are pressed for time.

We've selected some of the best calorie-consuming, fat-burning training sessions. Do two or three a

WHEN IS THE BEST TIME TO BURN CALORIES?

IF YOU'RE TRYING TO LOSE WEIGHT through running and gym workouts, is it better to burn calories by working out before eating, or afterward?

The timing of your meals won't change the number of calories burned during a workout (for running, that's about 100 calories per mile).

However, timing will affect how you feel and perform when you train. If you're not properly fueled up, a workout can leave you feeling tired and shaky, and this will compromise the intensity and duration of your exercise.

To make sure you have plenty of fuel in the tank, eat two to four hours before your workouts. Include easily digested foods that are high in carbohydrates—such as pasta, cereal, yogurt, fruits, and vegetables. To speed recovery, refuel immediately after your workouts with more carbohydrate-rich foods, plus a bit of protein from foods such as lean beef, chicken, or fish and fat-free milk or soy milk.

For optimum weight loss, it's also important to balance calorie intake with physical activity level throughout the day. Eat more when you are more active, and less when you are less active.

IMAGE: MITCH MANDEL

SCALE DOWN
Eat smaller portions
and the scales won't lie.

WEIGHT LOSS

week. On the other days, run easy for 20 to 30 minutes or do some relaxed cross-training such as cycling, swimming, or stair climbing.

LONG RUNS Run slowly for at least 45 minutes to an hour; one and a half to two hours would be ideal. The slow pace—which puts your metabolism in the fat-burning zone—coupled with the long period of time maximizes total fat burning. A 90-minute long run for a 170-pound man can burn more than 1,000 calories.

TEMPO RUNS If you have just 20 to 30 minutes to run, your best bet is to pick up the pace. The faster you run in those minutes, the more fat you'll burn, because your total energy cost is up. A 170-pound man on a 30-minute tempo run can burn more than 450 calories.

SPEED SESSIONS After a five-minute warmup, try running one to three minutes at 85- to 95-percent effort, then walk or jog for recovery. Do five to 10 of these fast intervals in a session, then finish with a five-minute cooldown. Speedwork also produces an "afterburn" effect. That is, you keep burning calories at a high level even after you've stopped running. This can sometimes amount to as much as 200 extra calories, and fast running suppresses your appetite for an hour or two, so you'll eat less and lose more.

A speed workout that includes 8 x 2 minutes at 90 percent effort (with a five-minute warmup and cooldown) can burn more than 700 calories (including afterburn) for a 170-pound man.

PUMP UP THE WEIGHT LOSS

By adding a once- or twice-weekly weight-training session to your schedule, you not only burn more calories when you are working out (115 every 30 minutes for our 170-pound runner)—but also when you are just sitting around. That's because as you add muscle, your resting metabolism rises. A good workout is circuit training—laps around the weight room, doing all the standard machine exercises, one right after another. When you can lift a weight 15 times easily, set it at a higher level. Five pounds is a good increase for upper-body exercises; 10 pounds for the lower body.

EATING STRATEGIES THAT BURN CALORIES

While you're revving up your running, ease back a little on your eating. Don't worry—you don't have to starve yourself. In fact, taking in too few calories slows your metabolism and makes it harder to lose weight. By simply making a few adjustments to your

usual diet, you can cut calories quickly.

You don't need a calorie counter to plan low-fat meals, just some common sense. Eat less, on the basis that your battle isn't against food, but against too much food. Learn to be polite but firm at Sunday dinner when your mom passes the roast potatoes the second time. When you eat at home, cut your serving size. "It's the number one way to cut calories," says John Allred, coauthor of *Taking the Fear out of Eating: A Nutritionist's Guide to Sensible Food Choices*. If you usually have two slices of bread with dinner, eat one. If you have six ounces of pasta, have four ounces.

Allred also suggests using smaller dinner plates. "That way, you still have a full plate of food in front of you, but you'll be eating less," he says.

The flip side is to eat more often. Many sumo wrestlers skip breakfast on purpose. They want to drive up hunger and slow their metabolism so when they dive into a fat-filled lunch, it sticks to their ribs (and bellies and sides) like glue. You, of course, don't want to look like a sumo wrestler. By eating three small meals a day, plus healthy snacks, you keep hunger on an even keel (avoiding overeating, the real enemy), and your metabolism runs at an even burn.

First, don't skip breakfast. Nancy Clark, author of *Nancy Clark's Sports Nutrition Guidebook*, says a good breakfast is one of the most potent weapons for losing weight. It keeps your metabolism turning over, prevents hunger and overeating at lunch, and makes

IMAGE: ALAMY

TALE OF THE TAPE
The right mix of running and nutrition will reduce your waistline.

WEIGHT-LOSS TIPS

SEE A DIETITIAN
It's not easy to determine which foods to eat to achieve the right ratio of carbs, protein, and fat, so consider calling in a professional. A registered dietitian can guide you in your food choices and fine-tune your weight-loss program.

AVOID FAD DIETS
Weight-reducing plans that have you radically changing your eating habits usually don't work in the long run. You can lose weight quickly, but it usually comes right back.

DON'T USE DIET PILLS
Unless you're clinically obese and at medical risk (you have diabetes or high blood pressure, for example), don't take diet pills. They don't eliminate the main reasons people overeat, which are often psychological.

KEEP A RECORD
Write down your weight loss. A visible record of your success can help motivate you to continue. It will show that you're making progress.

UNDERSTAND GENETICS
Your family history frequently dictates your physique. If your parents are big, you'll probably be big. You can't change this.

SHOP WITH A LIST
Avoid impulse purchases and impulse eating. Impulsive food choices often prove to be high-calorie ones.

you more likely to eat high-quality foods during the day. A good breakfast and afternoon snack will give you energy to burn.

You almost certainly know your weak spots (ice cream, chips, pizza, whatever). Set up a defense. If you crave ice cream, don't have it in the freezer. It's okay to indulge once in a while, but try the low-fat treats available, and consume them in moderation. Remember, despite the "healthy" labels, these snacks do still have plenty of calories, so eat them sparingly.

MAKE NEW HABITS

There are plenty of little things you can do with your diet that will make a big difference in your weight-loss efforts. Here are five of them:

DON'T MIX FAT AND SUGAR A burger, large fries, and soda is a bad combination to begin with, but it's doubly unhealthy because it acts as a hidden invitation to your body to pack on fat. The simple sugars in carbonated drinks cause a release of insulin into your bloodstream, which makes fat cells more prone to storing fat.

MAN CANNOT LIVE BY CARBS ALONE Protein and a little fat help keep you satiated for longer and prevent you from overeating. "Fat and protein stay with you longer," says Clark. For example, if you have a plain toasted bagel and fruit juice for breakfast, you'll be hungry again an hour later, but if you spread a little peanut butter on the bagel, you'll be fuller for longer.

EAT A COMPLEX DIET So you want loads of energy to burn all day? Eat lots of complex carbohydrates: fresh fruits, veggies, whole grains, and legumes. Complex carbs take longer to burn than simple sugars, giving you energy and staving off hunger at the same time.

HOLD THE MAYO Fish is a healthy option, right? But mixing tuna with mayonnaise adds hundreds of fat calories to a tuna-salad sandwich. Instead, try mixing the tuna with chile sauce, lemon juice, or mustard.

ONE STEP AT A TIME According to sports nutritionist Kris Clark, you'll have the most success changing a dietary habit if you take the simplest approach. "When I spot a problem in an athlete's food record, I have my clients stay with one dietary change for as long as it takes to become habit. Once we are successful with the first change, we can go on to the second."

It's like the way you learned to run. First one mile, then two…. It's the same thing with your diet. Take your time. Don't set unattainable goals. Stay focused on the task, and let patience and discipline work their magic.

11 SHORTCUTS TO FASTER FAT LOSS

Read on to reach your fat-loss finish line in the fastest way

1 GO LONG

Increase your total training mileage to 20 miles a week, and you'll lose abdominal fat even without decreasing your calorie intake, according to a report in the *Journal of Applied Physiology*. This is backed up by another study that found that substantial weight loss didn't occur unless running distances were more than 15.5 miles (25-K) per week for men, and 29.8 miles (48-K) per week for women.

2 LOW-FAT, SCHMO-FAT

Want to stay discomfort-free throughout your fat-shedding quest (and beyond)? Give low-fat diets a wide berth. Studies have revealed that runners who got less than 30 percent of their calories from fat were 2.5 times more likely to suffer injuries. Researchers believe this is due to a lower intake of vitamin K, deficiencies of which can increase the risk of bone fractures.

3 GO SOLO (IF YOU'RE A WOMAN)

Surely teaming up with your partner will spur you on to greater losses, right? Not according to one 16-month study reported in the *Archives of Internal Medicine*. Examining exercise for weight loss, and how it affects the genders, researchers discovered that with the same amount of exercise, the male participants lost 11.5 pounds, while the women only managed to maintain their weight.

4 BUY BELLY-BLITZING GEAR

Using a pedometer to track your mileage can motivate you to stay on your feet longer—and lose extra pounds—according to a study published by the *Journal of the American Medical Association*. A survey at Stanford University School of Medicine revealed that pedometer users tended to walk an extra mile a day compared with those who exercised without.

Nike+ Sportband measures distance, time, pace, and calories burned.

5 RUN STRONGER IN ONE WEEK

Shifting just 2.2 pounds—an average loss in the first week of a new regimen—can give your running a real boost, physically as well as mentally. "A 2004 study found that aerobic demand increases by one percent for every 2.2 pounds carried on the trunk," says Stan Reents, author of *Sports and Exercise Pharmacology*. While aerobic demand doesn't correlate directly with decreased performance, Reents says there's enough of a relationship to suggest that losing extra pounds can make a difference to your running performance.

6 STICK TO IT

Don't give up. Weight gained during off weeks can't be lost by simply resuming a previous routine, according to studies at the Lawrence Berkeley National Laboratory. Researchers say weight gain among those who decreased their weekly running distances was significantly more than weight loss among those who increased weekly distances by the same amount.

7 DO ONE "MARATHON" A WEEK

Calm down—you don't have to run a 26.2-miler every week. You can still feel the burn at a much slower pace. According to a study at the U.S. Institute of Medicine, people who walk 60 to 90 minutes a day—equivalent to covering a marathon a week—tended to shed at least 28 pounds in all and kept the weight off for six years.

8 8 IS THE MAGIC NUMBER

Running intervals? Eight-second blasts of effort are fat melters, say researchers at the University of New South Wales, Australia. They found that participants who followed a 20-minute cycling program, in which they sprinted on a stationary bike for eight seconds then cycled lightly for 12 seconds, lost more weight than those who cycled at a steady pace for 40 minutes.

9 FINISH FAST

Want to torch a few extra calories at the end of your training run? It's simple: Finish fast. "Choose a distance appropriate to your fitness and goals. Complete all but the last five minutes at a comfortable aerobic pace, then run at approximately your 5-K race pace," says coach Nick Anderson. A 150-pound runner will burn around 390 calories on a 30-minute run.

10 LOVE HILLS

Okay, they can be tough. But hills are certainly a fat-burning ally. "Generally you can count on a 10 percent increase in calories burned for each degree of incline," says Dr. Jana Klauer from St. Luke's–Roosevelt Hospital in New York City. "So running at a five percent incline will burn 50 percent more calories than running on a flat surface, and running on a 10 percent incline doubles your calorie burn."

11 KNOW YOUR BURN

When losing weight, the best way to keep up with your progress is by finding out how many calories you burn when you run, using your pace and weight, below:

PACE	130 LBS.	160 LBS.	190 LBS.
12 MIN/MILE	472 cals/hr	582 cals/hr	691 cals/hr
11 MIN/MILE	532 cals/hr	655 cals/hr	734 cals/hr
10 MIN/MILE	591 cals/hr	727 cals/hr	864 cals/hr
9 MIN/MILE	650 cals/hr	800 cals/hr	950 cals/hr
8 MIN/MILE	709 cals/hr	873 cals/hr	1,036 cals/hr
7 MIN/MILE	827 cals/hr	1,018 cals/hr	1,209 cals/hr
6 MIN/MILE	945 cals/hr	1,163 cals/hr	1,382 cals/hr

IMAGES: ALAMY

THE RUNNER'S GUIDE TO WEIGHT LOSS

**Conventional dieting wisdom doesn't work for runners.
It leaves you hungry, tired, and...overweight.
So we updated seven popular weight-loss strategies
to help you drop pounds for good**

DIETER'S STRATEGY		RUNNER'S STRATEGY
DEVELOP A RUNNING ROUTINE AND STICK TO IT	**VS.**	**MIX UP YOUR ROUTINE WITH NEW TYPES OF WORKOUTS**

Anyone trying to lose weight knows that he or she needs to work out on a nearly daily basis—and that's not easy. So to stay on track, dieters develop a workout routine (that often includes lots of steady, slowish runs) and then stick to it no matter what. "People are comfortable doing what they know," says Pete McCall, an exercise physiologist with the American Council on Exercise. "If you're a runner, you feel comfortable with a specific pace or distance."

Sticking to that routine brings dieters security. While running an easy three-miler a few days a week is better for weight loss than sprawling on the sofa, there is a smarter approach. Break out of your routine by boosting your intensity and doing different types of workouts (like a weekly long run or a day of cross-training) to challenge your body and burn more calories.

"It's a lot like city driving versus highway driving," says McCall. "When running a long, slow distance, your body becomes really efficient at using oxygen. The more times you do the same distance, the easier it gets and the fewer calories you burn. Sprinting is like starting and stopping a car, which uses more gas."

IMAGE: HUGH KRETSCHMER

WEIGHT LOSS

Though the fat-free craze peaked in the 1990s, many dieters still avoid oils, butter, nuts, and other fatty foods. Their logic: If you don't want your body to store fat, then don't eat fat. Many dieters also know that one gram of fat packs nine calories, while protein and carbohydrate both contain just four calories per gram.

But the logic of having fat in your diet has risen to the fore again. "I think it's a pretty antiquated thought now that we need to eliminate fat to lose weight," says Jonny Bowden, author of *The 150 Most Effective Ways to Boost Energy Naturally*. In fact, eating moderate amounts of fat can actually help you lose weight. The key is to make sure you're eating the right kinds.

Saturated and trans fats are unhealthy because they raise your levels of LDL (so-called "bad cholesterol"). Trans fats may also lower your HDL (or "good cholesterol") levels and increase your risk of heart disease and weight gain. But unsaturated fats (which include the mono- and polyunsaturated varieties) have important benefits. For example, they:

1 KEEP YOU SATISFIED

Unsaturated fats promote satiety, reduce hunger, and minimally impact blood sugar. That's important because if your blood sugar dips too low, you may experience cravings, brain fog, overeating, and low energy, making it "fiendishly difficult to lose weight," according to Bowden.

2 PROTECT HEART HEALTH

Monounsaturated fats found in vegetable oils (such as olive and canola oil) and avocados have the added power to help lower LDL and reduce your risk of heart disease.

3 REDUCE INJURY

Eating unsaturated fats can actually help stave off injuries, such as stress fractures. A 2008 study in the *Journal of the International Society of Sports Nutrition* found that female runners on low-fat diets particularly are at increased risk of getting injured—and of course a sidelined runner can't burn as many calories.

BREAK OUT OF A RUT

A 250-pound runner doing four miles at nine-minute-mile pace burns about 480 calories. But you can torch more calories by swapping that four-miler with one of these high-intensity workouts one to three times a week.

RUT BUSTER	WHAT	WHY	HOW	CALORIES BURNED
INTERVALS	Alternating sprints of a certain distance, such as 400 meters (m), with recovery laps; often done at a measured track.	Sprinting at high speeds makes your body work harder and burns up to 30 percent more calories to keep up with the demand.	≫4 x 400 m hard, separated by an easy 400 m recovery lap ≫8 x 200 m hard, separated by 200 m easy ≫4 x 100 m hard, walking back to the start between sprints	700
FARTLEK TRAINING	A less formal version of intervals; the term actually means "speed play" in Swedish.	Like interval workouts, fartlek sessions make your body burn more calories to match the demand of running faster.	On a 45-minute run, pick a tree about 50 m away. Run hard until you reach it, and then slow down until recovered. Keep alternating between landmarks.	540
HILL RUNS	This workout is exactly what it sounds like: running uphill for a period of time.	Hills require more force to overcome the angle of the incline, leading to a challenging cardio workout; it's also a great way to strengthen the larger muscles of the legs.	Find a steep hill of 40 m to 80 m. ≫Start with 10 reps, building to 20. Run up and jog back down. ≫5 runs at 50 percent max. ≫2 to 3 runs at 80 percent max; 1 sprint at max speed.	600

IMAGE: ALAMY

DIETER'S STRATEGY
CUT OUT CARBS TO LOSE WEIGHT

RUNNER'S STRATEGY
HAVE QUALITY CARBS IN EVERY MEAL

In the past decade, the Atkins diet and other low-carb spinoffs have become as popular as 100-calorie snack packs. It's understandable why dieters would find these plans attractive—just eat high-protein, high-fat foods, and shun carbs—to drop pounds. "The theory behind reducing carbs is that it helps control blood-sugar and insulin surges," says Bowden. "When you eat a high-carb food, insulin carries the sugar to muscles. But if your muscles don't use the energy, it gets stored in fat cells." This is what leads to weight gain.

It's a different story for runners, however. We need carbs because they're our main source of glucose, a sugar that our brains and muscles use as fuel. Most glucose is stored in muscles and the liver as glycogen and used as energy when we run. But the body can only store a limited amount of glycogen, so if you haven't eaten enough carbs, you'll literally run out of fuel.

Keeping carbs in your diet will have a domino effect, says sports nutritionist Barbara Lewin. Your energy levels will stay high, your workouts will improve, and you'll have more zip throughout the day. All this leads the way to a greater calorie burn and weight loss. Just keep in mind that "the kind of carbohydrates you eat makes all the difference in the world," says Bowden. Here's a quick guide to choosing the right ones for the right times:

1 SLOW-BURNING CARBS
These are high in fiber and are slowly digested. They keep your blood sugar steady, provide long-lasting energy, and should be a staple of your diet. Get them in oatmeal and other whole grains, beans, lentils, fruits, and vegetables.

2 FAST-BURNING CARBS
These carbs are digested quickly, are low in fiber, and have a greater effect on your blood sugar. They also provide a quick hit of energy that's useful to runners right before working out, but they should be eaten in moderation. Get them in pasta, white rice, white flour, potatoes, and cereals.

DIETER'S STRATEGY
CUT 500 CALORIES A DAY TO LOSE 1 POUND A WEEK

RUNNER'S STRATEGY
REDUCE CALORIE INTAKE BASED ON PERSONAL NEEDS

You've probably heard of the 500 rule: Slash 500 calories a day to lose one pound a week. "It's a nice, clean rule," says Lewin, and it can help weight loss—at least for a while. The problem for runners, though, is that slashing that many calories can be too much. "You might not be able to work out as well or maintain muscle mass," says Lewin. So rather than cut 500 calories, runners should work to identify how many calories they need to eat to lose weight. Here's how:

1 COUNT CALORIES
Track your intake by keeping a food journal for one week. Write down everything you eat, and note your energy and hunger levels on a scale of 1 to 10 (calorie counts for most foods can be found at nutritiondata.com).

2 TRIM, DON'T SLASH
Start by cutting 300 calories a day. If you're running, you'll still hit a 500-calorie deficit per day.

3 TWEAK IT
If you cut 300 calories but the scales haven't budged, it's time to reduce your intake gradually. You can also adjust according to your training.

SMALL CHANGES, BIG REWARDS

You don't need to make drastic adjustments to your calorie intake to start dropping pounds. Small substitutes here and there throughout the day can add up and lead to significant and sustainable weight loss. Nutritionist Kim Pearson suggests these simple food swaps to help cut calories while keeping your energy levels high.

SWAP OUT

Bagel with
cream cheese
360 calories

Starbucks
Grande Latté
190 calories

Snickers bar
280 calories

Subway six-inch roast-beef
sandwich on white with
mayo, cheese, and veggies
400 calories

1 cup of vanilla ice cream
290 calories

ORIGINAL CALORIE INTAKE
1,520

SWAP IN

1/2 whole-grain bagel
with peanut butter and
a cup of yogurt
325 calories

Starbucks
Grande Skinny Latté
130 calories

Kashi GoLean
Crisp Bar
180 calories

Subway six-inch roast-beef
sandwich on wheat with
mustard, no cheese, extra
veggies, and apple slices
on the side
340 calories

1/2 cup of vanilla ice cream
with a handful of
raspberries
205 calories

NEW CALORIE INTAKE
1,180

TOTAL SAVINGS 340 CALORIES

IMAGES: THOMAS MACDONALD

DIETER'S STRATEGY · VS · RUNNER'S STRATEGY
EAT DIET FOOD · EAT REAL FOOD

People think they need diet products in order to be successful," says Elaine Magee, R.N., author of *Food Synergy*. But all too often, the opposite is true. Runners can accomplish the same weight-loss goals while eating whole, real foods that taste better, provide more nutritional value, and are more satisfying.

"When you go for healthy whole foods, such as lean proteins, vegetables, fruits, whole grains, nuts and seeds, and low-fat dairy, you tend to get satiated on the right amounts," says Joy Bauer, R.N., author of *The Life Diet: Four Steps to Thin Forever*. The right real foods will help you lose, not gain, weight.

THREE REAL MEALS

Many diet foods are low in carbs, fiber, or protein, and won't keep you satisfied for long. Here, Magee offers a real, whole-foods recipe for each meal of the day in place of a "diet" choice. "While these are higher in calories than the diet options, they will help sustain your energy levels between meals," she says.

LUNCH
CURRIED CHICKEN SALAD SANDWICH

(Makes four sandwiches)
3 cups skinless chicken
breast, shredded
3 Tbsp. dried cranberries
3 Tbsp. toasted pine nuts
1 cup chopped apple
1/4 cup light mayonnaise
1/4 cup fat-free sour cream
1 Tbsp. honey mustard
1 tsp. curry powder

2 cups spring greens
or fresh spinach
8 slices multigrain, whole-
wheat, or sourdough bread,
or 4 whole-wheat pita breads

>> Toss together first
four ingredients. Whisk
mayonnaise, sour cream,
honey mustard, and curry
powder. Combine and serve.

BREAKFAST
MELON MANGO BREAKFAST SMOOTHIE

(Serves one)
3/4 cup frozen mango chunks
1/2 cup frozen or fresh
banana slices
1/2 cup cantaloupe, diced
1/3 cup low-fat vanilla yogurt
1/4 cup vanilla soy milk
(or low-fat milk with
1/4 tsp. vanilla)
1/4 cup low-fat granola
for topping

>> Place all of the
ingredients (except the
granola) in a food processor
or blender and purée until
thick and smooth (or lumpy if
that's how you like it). Spoon
into a dish or glass and
sprinkle granola over the top.

DINNER
FISH FILLETS WITH LEMON SAUCE

(Serves four)
1 pound fish fillets (sole,
halibut, or flounder)
1 1/2 cups Italian-style bread
crumbs
1 1/2 tsp. ground sage
2 tsp. Old Bay seasoning
2 large eggs
2 tsp. water
4 tsp. extra-virgin olive oil
2 Tbsp. lemon curd
2 Tbsp. whole milk
2 cups steamed brown rice
2 cups steamed broccoli

>> Combine bread crumbs,
sage, and seasoning. Mix
eggs and water in another
bowl. Heat oil in a pan. Dip
fillets in egg mixture, then
coat in crumbs. Place in pan.
Coat with olive oil spray.
Flip when brown (about four
minutes); cook other side.
Boil lemon curd and milk.
Serve with rice, sauce, and
broccoli.

IMAGES: MITCH MANDEL

WEIGHT LOSS

DIETER'S STRATEGY
DROP POUNDS FAST

 VS

RUNNER'S STRATEGY
LOSE POUNDS SLOWLY AND HAVE A POST-LOSS PLAN

For many dieters, their sole motivation is to lose weight as fast as possible. But this strategy leads them down a dangerous path. Once they hit their goal weight, dieters go back to their old habits, and soon enough the pounds creep back on.

"We often say, 'Hooray, I hit my goal weight. I'm done,'" says Linda Spangle, R.N., author of *100 Days of Weight Loss*. "That's the biggest mistake and stops you from maintaining it long-term." Just as you shouldn't stop training once you reach a running goal, keeping the weight off is a daily task. Here's how to be successful with your weight loss:

1 KEEP AT IT

Many "losers" continue high exercise levels and a reduced-calorie diet—two principles that got them to their new weight. "You can slowly increase your total calories if you remain very consistent with exercise—but do it gradually," says Spangle.

2 STEP ON THE SCALE

A review in the *International Journal of Behavioral Nutrition and Physical Activity* examined self-weigh-ing and weight gain. The conclusion: People who weigh themselves daily lose more weight—and keep it off.

3 GET SUPPORT

Finding some social support helps keep off the pounds. A 2007 study in *Obesity* showed that an online, therapist-led behavioral weight-loss Web site led to greater weight loss than a self-help commercial site.

4 BEWARE EMOTIONAL EATING

This is the number-one reason people regain weight, says Spangle. Plus, according to a 2008 *Nature* study, emotional eating often triggers binges. Ask yourself: "Does a bowl of chicken and broccoli sound good?" If not, you're not hungry for food as fuel.

5 KEEP YOUR MOTIVATION HIGH

Create a list of the reasons you want to lose weight. "It feels so good to be comfortable in your new body," says nutritionist Bauer. "Even if every day is a bit of a struggle, it's a struggle worth fighting."

POWERFUL STUFF

Ready to add strength training into your routine, but pressed for time? Exercise physiologist Pete McCall suggests adding the exercises here to your postrun routine. Start with one session per week and work up to three. Both exercises use a number of muscle groups, plus they're easy to do and take just a few minutes. "After 16 weeks, your waist measurement will shrink," he says.

SQUAT TO ROW

STRENGTHENS knees, quads, glutes, hips, back, core, and biceps

1 Stand two feet from a cable machine set at a weight that's hard but controllable.
2 Holding on to the cable handles with your arms extended, squat down.
3 As you rise up, pull your hands to your diaphragm. Do two or three sets of 12 to 15 reps.

WOOD CHOP

STRENGTHENS hips, quads, glutes, back, shoulders, and core

1 Stand with feet shoulder-width apart, holding a 5- to 8-pound medicine ball in your hands.
2 Squat down with the ball held in front of you, keeping your heels on the floor, sticking your bottom out, and not letting your knees go more than a few inches over your toes.
3 Return to standing, raising the ball overhead, maintaining a slight bend in your knees. Keep your core engaged the whole time, as if bracing for a punch. Do two or three sets of 12 to 15 reps; increase weight of the medicine ball when you can do 15 in good form.

IMAGE: CHRIS BROCK; ILLUSTRATIONS: KAGAN MCLEOD

BREAKING DOWN (WEIGHT-LOSS) BARRIERS

That pesky number on the scale not budging yet? You may have encountered a few roadblocks.

YOU'RE NOT GETTING ENOUGH SLEEP

Research has found that people who get less sleep eat more snacks. Without enough sleep, says Heather Gillespie, M.D., a sports-medicine physician at UCLA, your energy levels and immune system drop. But that doesn't mean you should cut out your morning runs to stay in bed. Routine is key for weight loss, so try going to bed earlier or switching your workouts to later in the day.

YOU EAT ENERGY-DENSE FOODS

A hamburger is an energy-dense food—so it packs more calories than less-dense foods, such as vegetable soup or a turkey sandwich. Less-dense foods have a higher water content than fats and carbs, and research has found that people who lower their energy density lower their weight. Those who eat a lot of energy-dense foods weigh more, have a higher intake of "bad" fats, and eat fewer fruits and vegetables.

YOU'RE STUCK IN A COLOR RUT

Many runners get the majority of their calories from carbs all the time. "I call it the flu diet," says nutritionist Lisa Dorfman, R.D. "Everything is bland and white." But research supports a colorful diet: Eating berries twice a day for eight weeks helps lower your blood pressure. "Eat at least five different colors daily," says Dorfman, "so that you can be assured you're getting enough fiber and protein."

YOU ONLY RUN

Running 15 miles a week burns roughly 1,500 calories—but to lose a pound, you need to cut 3,500 calories a week. In a study in the *American Journal of Physiology, Endocrinology and Metabolism*, researchers found that adults who cut their calorie intake by 300 calories a day lost nearly 25 percent of their body fat. People who only exercised lost just over 22 percent. Both regimens worked, but your best bet is to combine the effort.

DIETER'S STRATEGY
DON'T STRENGTH TRAIN

RUNNER'S STRATEGY
BALANCE RUNNING AND STRENGTH TRAINING

Dieters often shy away from strength training out of a fear it will make them bulk up. But for many dieters, the reason is simpler: They know one hour of intense cardio burns more calories than one hour of strength training.

Yet the truth is that taking the time to add strength training to your routine a few days a week has benefits that can boost your weight loss. Studies have shown that strength training can improve body composition and decrease your percentage of body fat, helping you look leaner and burn calories. Here's how it works:

1 MUSCLE BURNS CALORIES

"Fat burns almost nothing at rest," says exercise physiologist Pete McCall. "Muscle uses oxygen, so if you increase lean muscle mass, you'll raise the body's ability to use oxygen and burn calories." Your body typically uses up to seven calories per pound of muscle every day. If a 164-pound runner with 20 percent body fat increases his muscle mass and lowers his body fat to 15 percent, he'll burn an extra 36 to 56 calories a day at rest—simply by adding muscle.

2 YOU'LL BE MORE EFFICIENT

Strength training can help you run faster, longer, and more efficiently. A study in the *Journal of Strength and Conditioning Research* found that runners who add three days of resistance-training exercises to their weekly program increase leg strength and endurance. Runners with better endurance can run longer—and burn more calories. You'll also be able to recover faster from those long runs because strength training makes your body more efficient at converting metabolic waste into energy. "It's like being able to convert car exhaust fumes into gasoline," says McCall.

3 YOU'LL BE LESS INJURY-PRONE

"If you increase your strength, you'll also increase your joint stability," says McCall, citing a study in the *Journal of Strength and Conditioning Research*, which shows that doing squats, single-leg hops, and abs work not only prevents lower-body injuries but improves performance as well. Leg exercises can also reduce injury.

RUN IT OFF

Calorie-burning sessions to help you slim down and speed up

> **CRANKING UP THE INTENSITY** is the best way to take your running to the next level. It's also an effective way to burn extra calories and shed body fat. A 150-pound runner who picks up the pace from eight and a half minutes per mile to seven minutes per mile, for example, burns about 180 extra calories an hour. Should you speed up all of your runs dramatically? No, but the following five sessions include segments of higher-intensity running to boost your calorie burn. Try one or two per week, and include a five-minute warmup and cooldown.

1 JOE VIGIL'S ACCELERATIONS

Coach Joe Vigil designed this session for leg turnover and speed, but it also burns maximum calories in minimum time.

>**GO TO YOUR LOCAL TRACK,** or find a flat area where you can mark off 100 meters, and then every 10 meters after that up to 200 meters.

>**RUN 100 METERS** at roughly one-mile race pace. Note your time. Recover by walking from the finishing point back to the starting point.

>**RUN 110 METERS** slightly faster, so your 110-meter time is a second more than your 100-meter time.

>**CONTINUE** all the way up to 200 meters.

ESTIMATED BURN: 340 CALORIES

2 BRAD HUDSON'S MILES AND HILLS

Coach Brad Hudson, a former 2:13 marathon runner, likes to incorporate lots of short hill sprints into the sessions he prescribes. "They're great for developing running-specific strength," he says. Running hills also burns calories at a higher rate than running on flat terrain. This session combines hill sprints with 10-K-pace mile intervals.

>**RUN 2 X 1 MILE** at 10-K race pace. Follow each mile with three minutes' jogging for recovery.

>**RUN FOR 20 SECONDS** up part of a steep hill at maximum speed. Jog slowly for two minutes to recover. Do a total of five hill sprints.

ESTIMATED BURN: 466 CALORIES

3 MATT CENTROWITZ'S 10-K RACE PREP

Cross-country coach Matt Centrowitz is a big believer in sessions that closely simulate the demands of racing. This session will prepare you for a peak 10-K performance and incinerate a lot of calories.

>**RUN 800 METERS** roughly 20 seconds faster than your 10-K goal pace. For example, if your 10-K goal pace is eight minutes per mile, aim for 3:40. Walk or jog for two to three minutes for recovery.

>**RUN 800 METERS** roughly 10 seconds faster than your 10-K goal pace. Recover as above.

>**RUN TWO MILES** at your 10-K goal pace.

>**RUN 800 METERS** roughly 10 seconds faster than your 10-K goal pace.

>**RUN 800 METERS** roughly 20 seconds faster than your 10-K goal pace.

ESTIMATED BURN: 520 CALORIES

4 THE MONEGHETTI FARTLEK

Olympic marathoner Steve Moneghetti developed a fartlek session that alternates short bursts of fast and slow running to boost overall calorie burn.

>**RUN TWO SETS** of 90 seconds hard (five to 10 seconds per mile faster than 5-K pace), 90 seconds easy (45 to 50 seconds per mile slower than the hard runs).

>**RUN FOUR SETS** of 60 seconds hard, 60 seconds easy.

>**RUN FOUR SETS** of 30 seconds hard, 30 seconds easy.

>**RUN FOUR SETS** of 15 seconds hard, 15 seconds easy.

ESTIMATED BURN: 400 CALORIES

5 GREG MCMILLAN'S SUPERFAST FINISH

Coach Greg McMillan has done this session since his days as a school cross-country runner. Choose a running distance appropriate to your fitness level.

>**COMPLETE** all but the last five minutes at a comfortable aerobic pace.

>**RUN THE LAST FIVE MINUTES** at approximately 5-K race pace.

ESTIMATED BURN: 390 CALORIES FOR A 30-MINUTE RUN (without including a warmup or cooldown).

ILLUSTRATION: JOE MORSE

WOMEN'S HEALTH

The difference between men and women is not just visual when it comes to running—here are the things you need to know

> **APART FROM THE SORT** of injuries that can plague all runners—shinsplints, black toenails, tendinitis—there are some health issues that are more prevalent in women runners, and some that are exclusively female.

MENSTRUAL PROBLEMS

Although some women complain of discomfort during their periods, it is generally accepted that menstruation has limited impact on exercise performance. Women have run well, set records, and won championships at all phases of the menstrual cycle. Clinical studies have shown no change in heart rate, strength, or endurance during the cycle. Exercise can improve your feelings of well-being before and during your period, and some doctors recommend exercise for women who suffer discomfort at this time of the month.

A potential problem for runners is the cessation of menstruation. Women who run strenuously may be at higher risk of having "athletic amenorrhea," or irregular or absent periods. Training stress, performance pressure, low body fat, and inadequate nutrition are all possible contributing factors.

One of the most serious consequences of amenorrhea is osteoporosis, which happens because female hormones, which protect calcium in bone, are in short supply. An early onset of osteoporosis can lead to a greatly increased risk of stress fractures and acute fractures, and since decreased bone density is not easily reversed, it might last for the rest of your life.

An additional concern is lack of ovulation. Because women can menstruate even when not ovulating, the presence of a period does not guarantee a healthy menstrual cycle. A lack of ovulation can signal insufficient levels of progesterone, which can lead to overstimulation of the uterine lining, putting you at risk of endometrial cancer.

A woman's body temperature is generally lower at the beginning of her monthly cycle and higher for the last two weeks. The increase in temperature occurs at the time of ovulation. To track this cycle, take your temperature first thing in the morning. If your conditions point toward any sort of irregularity, consult your doctor.

"THE PILL"

Researchers disagree about the impact of oral contraceptives on athletic performance. Though most studies have shown that "the pill" has no effect on performance, some research indicates it may cause a slight reduction in aerobic capacity. On the other hand, some runners feel the pill helps performance by reducing menstrual symptoms. These runners prefer taking the pill so they can control their cycle and don't have to race when they are having their period. Although it is safe to manipulate the timing of your period, experts generally agree that this practice should be reserved for major competitions and done only a few times a year.

If you run recreationally, you probably don't have to worry about any athletic impact of the pill. But if you race and don't want to risk sacrificing aerobic capacity, consider another type of contraception.

OSTEOPOROSIS

Exercise can help build and maintain bone-density levels in women, but women who have abnormal menstrual cycles may not gain these benefits.

Several studies have shown women who have

disrupted menstrual cycles suffer more stress fractures than their counterparts with normal cycles. These women typically exhibit lower levels of bone-mineral density. Although it's generally accepted that hormonal disruptions and premature loss of bone density are linked in female athletes, the cause-and-effect relationship is not clear. For example, some researchers think the kind of woman drawn to intense exercise is more likely to exhibit stress in all areas of life, which could affect hormone levels even without exercise.

Experts agree that women must act to protect themselves from early-onset osteoporosis. It's particularly important because once she's past the mid-30s, a woman can no longer build bone mass, but only maintain her reserves. You should take every precaution to ensure that you are not losing bone mass. That means eating a properly balanced diet—in addition to all the important nutrients, and calcium in particular, you should make sure you are consuming enough fat and calories overall to sustain your level of exercise. Monitor your menstrual cycle, and if there are any irregularities, consult with your doctor.

INCONTINENCE

Women are more prone to stress incontinence because of their anatomy. It's estimated that one in two women experience some level of urine leakage, and it is annoying and disconcerting.

Although running does not cause incontinence, the activity can induce leakage in women who are already prone to it. Many women find relief by strengthening the muscles in the pelvic area with Kegel exercises. To do these, contract your pelvic muscles as if you are attempting to stop a flow of urine. Hold for a few seconds, and then release. There are also several devices that can be bought over the counter or with a prescription that help control leakage. Talk to your doctor about what might work best for you.

ACNE

Women runners can be plagued by skin breakouts on their face, hairline, upper back, chest, upper arms, and buttocks. Sweat production combined with hair follicles or friction from rubbing clothes is a formula for acne. Increased temperature and humidity exacerbate the problem, as do products such as sunscreen and makeup, which sweat off onto the skin and clog pores.

LOOKING GOOD
Running is great, but women are more prone to certain problems than men are.

HOW TO FEND OFF ACNE

> Minimize the use of makeup and hair-care products before running. Wash your face before running, and again before reapplying makeup.

> Use a sunscreen specifically formulated for the face on your face and neck. Choose a gel or lotion for the rest of your body, rather than a cream.

> Wipe acne-prone areas with an astringent pad or towelette immediately after running. Once your body's natural oils cool, they harden, which can lead to plugged pores.

> Change out of sweaty exercise clothes right after running, and shower as soon as possible.

> Cleanse acne-prone areas thoroughly. Gentle exfoliation can help, but don't scrub to the point of aggravating your skin.

> If you are prone to acne, consult a dermatologist.

IMAGE: GUIDO VITTI

21 TIPS FOR WOMEN RUNNERS

You shouldn't need an excuse to get out there, but there are plenty of very good reasons to slip those shoes on right now

> **KNOWLEDGE IS POWER,** in running as in any other pursuit. The more you know about training, nutrition, and health, the better you'll be at maximizing your running, whether that means fitness, weight loss, great race performances, or just plain fun. In this section, you'll find loads of information to help you reach your goals.

These facts and tips cover health, psychology, weight loss, pregnancy, motherhood, training, racing, and more, and address the specific needs of women to help you become the runner you want to be.

1 ANAEROBIC RESULTS

For female runners, controlled anaerobic training—intervals, hills, fartlek training—may lead to gains in strength and speed similar to those produced by steroids, but without the noxious side effects. Why? High-intensity anaerobic running is one of the most potent stimulators of natural human growth hormones—those that contribute to stronger muscles and, ultimately, enhanced performance.

2 FIRST THINGS FIRST

Running early in the morning means you can get the sweaty business out of the way before applying makeup and dressing for work. But perhaps more important, statistics show that women are more likely to be attacked later in the day. Don't be scared off, but do take precautions. More on that later.

3 RUNNING WITH CHILD

Doctors consider moderate exercise during a normal pregnancy to be completely safe for the baby. Running should cause no problems in the first trimester, and it should be fine for most people in the second trimester. Few women would run in their final three months, however. The most important precaution is to avoid becoming overheated; a core body temperature above 100.4°F could increase the risk of birth defects. So make sure you're staying cool enough, and if in doubt, take your temperature after a run. If it's over 101°F, you're probably overdoing it. Also, skip that postrun soak in a hot bath.

4 SHOE SELECTION

Women generally have narrower feet than men, so when buying running shoes, you're best off going for a pair designed specifically for women. That said, everyone's different, so if your feet are wide, you may feel more comfortable in shoes designed for men. The bottom line: Buy the shoe that's best for you. If there's any question—or if you suffer blisters or injuries because of ill-fitting shoes—consult a podiatrist who specializes in treating runners.

IMAGE: EMBRY RUCKER

NOW JUST $1.17 AN ISSUE

RUNNER'S
EXCLUSIVE REPORTS
Find Your **BLISS**

RUNNER'S
EXCLUSIVE REPORTS
Running **SHOE BASICS**

RUNNER'S
EXCLUSIVE REPORTS
STRETCH It Out

RUNNER'S
EXCLUSIVE REPORTS
SUPER-FOODS for Runners

RUNNER'S
EXCLUSIVE REPORTS
HIT THE ROAD

RUNNER'S
EXCLUSIVE REPORTS
Your Best 5-K or 10-K

RUNNER'S
EXCLUSIVE REPORTS
How to Run FOREVER

RUNNER'S
EXCLUSIVE REPORTS
GET FIT to Run

RUNNER'S
EXCLUSIVE REPORTS
Keep Your **MENTAL EDGE**

RUNNER'S
EXCLUSIVE REPORTS
WEIGHT LOSS Strategies

PLUS YOU GET 0 FREE VALUABLE RUNNING REPORTS!

Just $1.17 an issue
(with this card)

DO YOU RUN TOO MUCH?
RUNNER'S
Fit & Healthy Forever
Train Smart Eat Right Avoid Injury & Other Lessons From A Lifetime of Running
Meb's Amazing Year
STRESS LESS Easy Ways to Calm
BEGINNERS
SAVE 77%
Pre-Run Breakfast
BRILLIANT! Ingenious Ideas Discovered On the Run
REVOLUTION And the Who Started It All

Best Deal!
☐ **2 years (24 issues) just $23** (plus $4.97 shipping)
☐ 1 year (12 issues) just $16 (plus $3.97 shipping)

Plus I get my 10 Free Reports!

RWD K3F9Y10A

Name _____

Address _____ Apt #

City _____ State ____ ZIP

Send no money now. We can bill you later.

Canada: 1 yr., CDN $29.96 (includes all applicable Canadian taxes). International: 1 yr: U.S. $60 prepaid. Please allow 4-6 weeks for delivery.

24/2797 \ 12/1997   202285001 / Printed in USA   ♻ Printed on recyclable paper

10 FREE RUNNING REPORTS!

30% Post Consumer Waste
Printed on Recycled Paper.

NO POSTAGE
NECESSARY
IF MAILED
IN THE
UNITED STATES

BUSINESS REPLY MAIL
FIRST-CLASS MAIL   PERMIT NO. 54   LEHIGH VALLEY, PA

POSTAGE WILL BE PAID BY ADDRESSEE

RUNNER'S WORLD
PO BOX 26299
LEHIGH VALLEY PA 18003-9911

NOW
JUST
$**1**.17

AN
ISSUE

PLUS YOU
GET 10 FR▶
RUNNING
REPORTS
◀ Detach and return ca

LIMBER UP
These women-friendly
tips will get you on
the right track.

5 REDUCE CANCER RATES

An American study found that running women produce a less potent form of estrogen than their sedentary counterparts. As a result, female runners cut by half their risks of developing breast and uterine cancer, and by two-thirds their risk of contracting the form of diabetes most common in women.

6 SISTERS UNITED

Having another woman or a group of women to run with regularly will help keep you motivated and ensure your safety. It's also a lot more fun than running alone. Women runners become more than training partners; they're confidantes, counselors, and coaches, too.

7 KEEP IT REAL

Women who run for weight control may lose perspective on what is an appropriate body size. A recent survey of thousands of women found that while 44 percent of respondents were medically overweight, 73 percent thought they were.

8 CALCIUM AND IRON

The two minerals women runners need to pay the most attention to are calcium and iron (iron is especially important for menstruating women). Good sources of calcium are dairy products, dark leafy vegetables, broccoli, canned sardines, and salmon, while foods high in iron include liver, fortified dry cereals, beef, and spinach.

9 GET TESTED

Women who train intensively, have been pregnant in the past two years, or consume fewer than 2,500 calories a day should conduct more than routine blood tests for iron status, since these test only for anemia, the final stage of iron deficiency. Ask for more revealing tests, such as those for serum ferritin, transferrin saturation, and total iron-building capacity.

10 PERIOD GAINS

There's no need to miss a run or a race just because you're having your period. If you're suffering from cramps, running will often alleviate the pain, thanks to the release during exercise of pain-relieving chemicals called endorphins. Speedwork and hill sessions can be especially effective, but use a tampon and a panty liner for extra protection.

NO SWEAT
Women perspire less than men, but still beware of dehydration.

11 SKIN WINS

Running helps produce healthy skin. According to dermatologists, running stimulates circulation, transports nutrients, and flushes out waste products. All of this leads to a reduction in subcutaneous fat, making skin clearer and facial features more distinct.

12 IGNORE TAUNTING

It may not be much consolation, but men are sometimes verbally harassed and occasionally threatened while running, just as women are. Be sensible when you run, but don't let insignificant taunting limit your freedom.

13 DON'T OVERDO IT

If you run so much your periods become light or nonexistent, you may be endangering your bones. Amenorrhea (lack of a monthly period) means that little or no estrogen, essential for the replacement of bone minerals, is circulating in your body. You can stop, but not reverse, the damage by taking estrogen and plenty of calcium. If your periods are infrequent or absent, consult a gynecologist.

IMAGE: JASON GOULD

16 CHEST SUPPORT

No matter what your size, it's a good idea to wear a sports bra when you run. Look for one that stretches horizontally but not vertically. Most important, try before you buy. A sports bra should fit snugly, yet not feel too constrictive. Run or jump in place to see if it gives you the support you need.

17 LATE PREGNANCY AND BIRTH

If you run early in your pregnancy, you might want to try switching to a lower-impact exercise during the latter stages and after delivery. Due to the release of the hormone relaxin during pregnancy, some ligaments and tendons might soften, making you more vulnerable to injury, especially around your pelvis. Walking, swimming, stationary cycling, and aqua-running are good choices.

18 MONTHLY MOMENTS

"That time of the month" is not the time when women run their worst. The hardest time for women to run fast is about a week before menstruation begins (a week after ovulation). That's when levels of the key hormone progesterone peak, inducing a much-higher-than-normal breathing rate during physical activity. The excess ventilation tends to make running feel more difficult.

19 MAKING TIME

Just because you're married and have young children and a job doesn't mean you don't have time to run. Running is time-efficient and the best stress-reducer on the market. You need this time. Taking it for yourself (by letting your husband babysit while you run, for instance) will benefit the whole family.

20 BREASTFEEDING

Some studies have suggested that babies dislike the taste of post-exercise breast milk, because it is high in lactic acid and may impart a sour flavor. These studies are not conclusive, but you may like to either express milk for later feeding, or breast-feed before running.

21 WOMEN SWEAT LESS THAN MEN

However, contrary to popular belief, women dissipate heat as well as men. The reason: Women are smaller and have a higher body-surface-to-volume ratio, which means that although their evaporative cooling is less efficient, they need less of it to achieve the same result. Nonetheless, be sure to drink plenty of water to prevent dehydration.

14 STRONGER BABIES

If you were a regular runner before you got pregnant, you might have a bigger baby—good news, because, up to a certain point, larger infants tend to be stronger and weather physical adversity better. Researchers in the United States found that women who burned up to 1,000 calories per week through exercise gave birth to babies weighing five percent more than the offspring of inactive moms. Those who burned 2,000 per week delivered babies weighing 10 percent more.

15 IN THE INTEREST OF SAFETY

Women who run alone should take precautions. Leave a note at home stating when you left, where you'll be running, and when you expect to return. Carry a cell phone. Stick to well-populated areas, and don't always run the same predictable route. Avoid running at night, and don't wear jewelry. Pay attention to your surroundings and recurring faces. Carry identification, but include only your name and an emergency phone number.

TWO FOR THE ROAD

Becoming pregnant needn't mean your running has to fall by the wayside. It can benefit you both

> **"IT WAS A BEAUTIFUL WINTER DAY**—snowy but sunny—and I felt great running on snow-packed roads. I was as pregnant as possible—that evening, I gave birth. I had gone out for a five-miler, but I felt I could have run forever. No matter how much time passes, I can still mentally put myself on that road. A perfect run on a perfect day."

Okay, you're not an Olympic champion like Joan Benoit Samuelson, from whose book *Running for Women* this quote is taken. But if you're a pregnant runner who wants to maintain her fitness, your running doesn't have to suffer. While adhering to certain principles to ensure your health and that of your baby, as an expectant mom you can enjoy running much the same as in your nonexpectant condition.

First and foremost, it's crucial to listen to medical advice. A frank and open discussion with your doctor—about your overall health but particularly about your exercise program—is essential.

A supportive midwife or doctor who recognizes the benefits of an exercise program will not only listen to your concerns, but should also address your individual needs, although you shouldn't hesitate to seek a second opinion if you're uncomfortable with your initial diagnosis. Your well-being and peace of mind, as well as the livelihood of your baby, are at stake, so don't be afraid to speak up.

If you've been given the green light to run, proceed with cautious enthusiasm, says Rod Jaques, M.D., medical advisor to the British Triathlon Team at the British Olympic Medical Center. The health benefits to women who exercise while pregnant have been well documented. They include less lower-back pain, reduced amounts of analgesic at delivery, fewer instances of cesarean-section deliveries, and fewer cases of postnatal depression. What's more, women who exercise during pregnancy gain less weight, have improved mood and sleep patterns, and lose weight more rapidly after giving birth. Although now is not the time to begin a running program, if you're already a runner, then there's no reason to stop—just modify.

HOW INTENSE IS TOO INTENSE?

Dr. Jaques notes that concrete answers to the questions of "How much and at what intensity?" will never be found on the research block, since scientists will be hard-pressed to find a woman willing to subject her pregnancy to such experiments. But Dr. Jaques advises women to keep their heart rate at or below 140 beats per minute (bpm) while exercising.

CHILL OUT AND RELAX

Some research shows an internal body temperature above 100.4°F may cause birth defects in the developing fetus; yet other studies fail to confirm these findings. Given such conflicting reports, however, most experts agree that a pregnant woman must keep her core body temperature at a recognized safe level (below 100.4°F) to protect her unborn baby

HEALTH BENEFITS TO WOMEN WHO EXERCISE WHILE PREGNANT ARE WELL DOCUMENTED.

IMAGES: JILLIAN EDELSTEIN, GETTY

LIFTING THE PRIZE
Paula Radcliffe won the New York City Marathon 10 months after giving birth to Isla.

from potential birth defects, particularly to the fetus's central nervous system.

What can an expectant mother do to stay cool? In addition to keeping your heart rate at or below 140 bpm, experts advise you to train outdoors, rather than indoors on a treadmill where the wind's cooling effect is eliminated. If you are inside, be sure the area is well ventilated; keep the windows open and consider investing in a fan or two. Avoid running in very warm and hot conditions. Pregnant women should never run to the point of breathlessness or exhaustion—it's important to work to a comfortable level and not overdo it. You should additionally ensure you remain very well hydrated before, during, and after a run. Dr. Jaques advises pregnant athletes to drink three ounces of water every 15 minutes during a run, and to keep pumping the fluids afterward.

During pregnancy, a woman's body produces the hormone relaxin, which relaxes joints and ligaments. Loose joints and ligaments can make you more susceptible to injury, and the gradual widening of your hips will change your biomechanics and make your feet more likely to overpronate. Easing gently into a run and stretching properly afterward will help prevent injuries, as will choosing shoes with increased stability and cushioning.

According to the United Kingdom's National Childbirth Trust, during the first trimester of pregnancy you may experience increased tiredness, nausea, breast tenderness, pressure on your bladder, and constipation. Many of the side effects of pregnancy are due to the sudden rush of hormones in your body. Yet many women surveyed by Dr. Jaques report having "a wonderful time" when running during their first trimester. Be sure to map out toilet stops along your route, wear a supportive nonunder-wire bra, and stop running if you feel too tired at this stage. Weeks 1 to 12 are crucial as far as your baby's development goes.

From weeks 12 to 28, your pregnancy begins to show, and your breasts grow as milk-producing cells develop. Many women experience lower-back pain at this time due to the increased pressure on their pelvis; this may contribute to other unexpected pain, such as knee strain. With the added weight, your running gait may change, so be alert to terrain and traffic while running.

During the last lap of pregnancy, your weight

BUMP IN THE ROAD

Paula Radcliffe's postpartum 2007 ING New York City Marathon win begs the question: Is there an athletic benefit to pregnancy? Although no definitive link has been proven, the biological tools needed to build a baby could boost a new mom's performance. During pregnancy, blood volume goes up by as much as 40 percent. "Pregnancy makes you hypertrained. Your body becomes very efficient at circulating oxygen," says Nadya Swedan, M.D., author of *The Active Woman's Health and Fitness Handbook.* "If you begin running within weeks of giving birth, you can capitalize on those...gains."

That said, right after giving birth, Radcliffe suffered a stress fracture in her sacrum. "Your bones can get leached of calcium, which makes them susceptible," says Dr. Swedan. What's more, relaxin, which causes joints and ligaments to loosen up so the hips can accommodate birth, doesn't depart the body until at least four months postpartum, making you more prone to sprains.

IMAGES: ALAMY

BACK UP AND RUNNING
New moms are short on time, but you can make your baby part of your workout.

into shape.

Dr. Jaques explains that a woman may begin vigorous training from six weeks to three months following delivery—three months is more likely if there were any complications, but since everyone is different, it's important to listen to your own body.

After pregnancy, the increased plasma volume in your bloodstream may spur recovery. After being mentally starved of running, you may have more appetite for it. With less time on your hands, concentrate on quality sessions, which lead to an improved running performance.

MILKING THE SYSTEM

If you've decided to breastfeed your baby, then here's some good news: It seems exercise does not affect the quality or quantity of a mother's milk.

It's been widely reported that breastfed babies are less likely to suffer from gastrointestinal problems, diarrhea, respiratory problems, ear infections, pneumonia, and food allergies than formula-fed babies.

Some things to bear in mind: It's a good idea to breastfeed your baby before going out for a run. Keep note of your weight loss. If you're losing more than one pound a week, then add nutritious snacks to your diet in between meals. And eat healthy, well-balanced meals and stay properly hydrated. For more information on breastfeeding, contact the La Leche League (lalecheleague.org), a breastfeeding support group.

gain—finally—will begin to slow down. You may experience a shortness of breath and your feet may swell, making running taxing. Dr. Jaques notes: "It would take a heroic woman who would consider running during this stage of pregnancy. Physically, it's extremely challenging." Concentrated weight gain at the bottom of the sternum and pubic bone makes it difficult, biomechanically, to run.

Add to that the increased back pain, and running begins to seem a rather uncomfortable and painful—though not impossible—proposition. At this point it may be time to consider alternatives to running, such as swimming, cycling, low-impact aerobics, or walking.

GETTING BACK IN THE SWING

Returning to your pre-pregnancy running form largely depends upon two things: the type of birth you experience and your fitness level. In a normal birth, a woman can most likely begin exercising again when she feels no pain. But it is advised she wait around six weeks before beginning any aerobic exercise.

If you have a cesarean section, talk to your midwife or obstetrician. Residual scarring and bleeding may interfere with your ability to return to proper form as soon as you may like. Remember to take it slow. Low-impact exercises, such as walking and swimming, are good choices to ease you back

TOP TIPS

>> **TALK TO YOUR DOCTOR OR MIDWIFE** Find out their attitude toward combining exercise with pregnancy.

>> **TRAIN, DON'T STRAIN** Forget about speedwork and long endurance runs. Pay attention to your level of exertion, heart rate, and temperature.

>> **DON'T OVERHEAT** Run in the most temperate part of the day. Drink plenty of fluids before, during, and after a run.

>> **KNOW WHEN TO STOP** Cease running if you begin cramping or gasping for air, or feel dizzy. If you experience pain or bleeding or your water breaks, get medical attention immediately.

>> **CONSIDER YOUR OPTIONS** If running is becoming uncomfortable, try swimming.

>> **EAT WELL** Be sure you're getting enough iron, calcium, folic acid, and other nutrients.

>> **GO EASY** Running to the point of exhaustion doesn't do you or your baby any good.

YOUR FIRST 5-K

With the right advice, any runner can become a racer in just five weeks. How? Read on

> **FOR ONE BRIEF MOMENT,** probably while endorphins were still pumping through your body after a good run, you flirted with the idea of doing a marathon. Then the endorphins disappeared and the reality of training for four months and trying to squeeze in a handful of three- to four-hour-long runs set in. Fair enough. But how about a simple 5-K instead?

It's a perfect distance: 3.1 miles require relatively little buildup, the training doesn't take over your life, and the race is over fairly quickly. And by logging only three or four runs per week, you can be ready to toe the line of a 5-K in just five weeks.

Top coach Chris Carmichael encourages all runners to try a 5-K. "People run for a variety of reasons, but they get more out of it when they're working toward something specific," he says. "And a 5-K race is an attainable goal for any runner." Plus, there's the "fun factor," says Jeff Galloway, author of *Running: Getting Started.* "My favorite thing about 5-K races is the atmosphere. Almost everyone there is in a good mood. How many other events in your life are like that?"

THE FIVE-WEEK PLAN

In the five weeks leading up to your first 5-K, most coaches agree that you need to run three or four days a week. During one of those weekly runs, you should focus on increasing the amount you can run at one time until you build to at least the race distance, or the equivalent amount of time spent running. "I encourage runners, particularly beginners, to focus on time and effort, rather than becoming obsessed with miles and distance," says coach Nick Anderson of Great Britain. "Thinking in minutes is more gradual and self-paced and will help make sure you

don't get injured by doing too much too soon." Completing the equivalent of the 5-K distance in training gives you the strength and confidence you need to finish the race. And if you increase your long run up to six miles (or about twice the amount of time it should take you to cover the 5-K, or 3.1 miles), you'll run with even greater strength (or speed, if that's your thing).

Most of your running during the week should be at a comfortable pace. This is especially true for runners who simply want to finish the race. But because adding some faster training to your schedule is the best way to improve your speed and endurance, even novices should consider doing some quicker running. "Intervals are not reserved for elites," says Carmichael. "Running three one-mile intervals with recovery in between will do more to increase your sustainable running pace than running three miles at once." First-time racers can do some

"MY FAVORITE THING ABOUT 5-K RACES IS THE ATMOSPHERE. ALMOST EVERYONE THERE IS IN A GOOD MOOD."

ILLUSTRATION: KOREN SHADMI

5 WEEKS TO YOUR FIRST 5-K

It's training time. New runners who need to build up to the distance should follow the Beginner Plan.
Regular runners who've never raced a 5-K can try the Intermediate Plan.

>>BEGINNER PLAN

WEEK	MON	TUE	WED	THU	FRI	SAT	SUN
1	WALK/XT 20 min or day off	RUN 10 min	WALK/XT 20 min or day off	RUN 15 min	WALK/XT 20 min or day off	REST	RUN 2 miles
2	WALK/XT 20 min or day off	RUN 15 min	WALK/XT 20 min or day off	RUN 20 min	WALK/XT 20 min or day off	REST	RUN 2.5 miles
3	WALK/XT 30 min or day off	RUN 20 min	WALK/XT 30 min or day off	RUN 25 min	WALK/XT 30 min or day off	REST	RUN 3 miles
4	WALK/XT 30 min or day off	RUN 25 min	WALK/XT 30 min or day off	RUN 30 min	WALK/XT 30 min or day off	REST	RUN 3 .5 miles
5	WALK/XT 30 min or day off	RUN 30 min	WALK/XT 30 min or day off	RUN 30 min	WALK/XT 30 min or day off	REST	5-K RACE

BEGINNER PLAN KEY> WALK/XT DAYS: You can walk or cross-train (swim, bike, elliptical trainer, etc.) at a moderate intensity for the stated amount of time, or take the day off. **WEEKDAY RUNS:** All weekday runs should be at a steady, comfortable pace.
WEEKEND LONG RUN: This is measured in miles, rather than minutes, to ensure you increase the distance you cover each week. Long-run pace should be two or three minutes per mile slower than the pace you can run one mile flat-out. Feel free to take walk breaks.

>>INTERMEDIATE PLAN

WEEK	MON	TUE	WED	THU	FRI	SAT	SUN
1	3 miles plus 5 x strides	REST	4 miles plus 5 x strides	REST	4 miles plus 5 x strides	2 to 3 miles; 15-min core workout	REST
2	3 miles plus 5 x strides	REST	4 miles with 2 x 5 min at SS intensity; 15-min core workout	REST	3 miles plus 5 x strides	5 to 6 miles; 15-min core workout	REST
3	3 miles plus 6 x strides	REST	4 miles with 3 x 5 min at SS intensity; 15-min core workout	REST	3 miles plus 6 x strides	6 miles with the last 15 min at SS intensity; 15-min core workout	REST
4	3 miles plus 6 x strides	REST	4 miles with 2 x 10 min at SS intensity; 15-min core workout	REST	3 miles plus 5 x strides	6 miles with the last 15 min at SS intensity; 15-min core workout	REST
5	3 miles plus 4 x strides	REST	3 miles; 15-min core workout	REST	2 miles	2 miles plus 3 x strides	5-K RACE

INTERMEDIATE PLAN KEY> WEEKLY MILEAGE: Except where noted, weekly mileage should be run at a perceived effort (PE) of 6 out of 10. **STRIDES:** After completing the run, run hard for 20 seconds and recover with easy jogging or walking for 45 seconds; repeat as instructed. **CORE WORKOUT:** Do a series of basic exercises to strengthen core muscles and improve posture. **SS INTENSITY:** Intervals at Steady State Intensity should be run at a PE of 7 or 8. Do five minutes of easy running between SS intervals.

faster running one or two days a week, but these sessions don't have to be regimented. Anderson recommends adapting one session per week to include about 10 minutes of speedwork, made up of two five-minute runs at a faster pace, each framed by five minutes of jogging. Once this becomes easy, try one 10-minute interval at threshold pace—this is about 85 percent of your maximum heart rate, where you can utter a few words but not hold a conversation. Always bookend harder runs with easy warmup and cooldown jogs.

THE BIG DAY

The greatest challenge of running a 5-K is finding the right pace, says Anderson. Start out too fast and you might struggle to finish. That's why Galloway recommends that all first-time racers (including veteran runners) get to the back of the pack at the starting line. This prevents an overzealous start and allows you to gradually build up speed, ideally running the final mile the fastest.

But how fast should you expect to run come race day? While Carmichael says the main goal should be to have fun, he tells experienced runners who are new to racing that they can expect to race about 30 seconds per mile faster than training pace. So, runners training at a nine-minute-per-mile pace should finish in around 26:25; those training at a 10-minute-mile pace should finish in 29:31; and those training at an 11-minute-mile pace should finish in around 32:39.

Galloway has a different way of predicting race times. Every two weeks, his clients run a mile on a track as fast as they can. Then he uses a pace calculator, like the one at runnersworld.com, to predict their times for longer distances. In general, he finds that most runners slow down about 33 seconds per mile when they go from a one-mile run to 5-K race.

However, most experts discourage first-timers from shooting for strict time goals. "Make it a race against yourself," says Carmichael, "because it's your progress that's most valuable to you." Galloway seconds that. "If you enjoy it, you'll do it again." And probably faster.

FIRST-TIME FIVER?

Run like a road-racing pro by avoiding these three common first-time mistakes.

1 TOO FAST, TOO SOON "Most first-time racers go out too fast and are miserable by the second mile," says Anderson. **EASY FIX** Start out at a comfortable pace with no huffing and puffing. Move up gradually through the gears in the second half of the race until you are running hard for the last half-mile.

2 TOO MUCH FOOD Many first-timers eat too much before a race, particularly the night before. Most people have enough stored energy in their bodies to run a 5-K without taking in any additional calories. **EASY FIX** "Eat normally before the race," says Anderson. Try small meals the day before. On race day, eat a carbohydrate breakfast, but the key is being hydrated. Have water and fruit juice or sports drink.

3 TOO LITTLE WARMUP/ COOLDOWN Your body needs to warm up properly before it can run well at the higher intensity required to race a 5-K. And a postrace cooldown helps you recover more quickly so that you'll feel better the day after the race. **EASY FIX** Include a 15-minute warmup before the race, and a 15-minute cooldown after. For both, mix walking and jogging to help ease into and out of your race pace.

PIN DOWN A GOAL
You will get more out of your running if you work toward a race.

IMAGE: ALAMY

THE ULTIMATE 10-K PLAN

It's the classic distance—long enough to test your endurance, short enough for you to switch on the afterburners. Here's how to perfect your 10-K

> **YOU'LL BE GLAD** to hear that 10-K training forms the ideal foundation of almost all types of running performance. That's because it includes ample amounts of the three core components of distance training: strength, stamina, and speed. Obviously, you can use it to train for your goal 10-K, but with certain adjustments you can also use it to prepare for everything from the 5-K to the marathon. This is the classic distance, made famous by Ethiopian legends Haile Gebrselassie and Kenenisa Bekele. So read through the runner profiles below, and decide which of our six-week plans is best for you, but remember that these are not one-size-fits-all plans. If you can't complete a given session, you don't have to, and if you need to rearrange training days to fit your schedule, do so.

WHO AM I?

> **BEGINNER** You're a notch above novice. You've been running at least six months, and may have done a 5-K or two. You run three to five miles, three or four days a week; have done a little fast running when you felt like it; and now you want to enter—and finish—what you consider to be a real distance race.
> **INTERMEDIATE** You've been running a year or more, have done some 5-Ks and maybe even a 10-K, but you've always finished feeling as if you could have gone faster. You consider yourself mainly a recreational runner, but you still want to make a commitment, and see how fast you can go.

>> BEGINNER

If you are a beginner, your 10-K goal should be less about achieving a personal record (PR) than an LDF (longest distance finished). You want to run the whole 6.2 miles, so your main aim is endurance, because it's likely to take you an hour to get there. "Basic aerobic strength is every runner's first need," says running coach Bud Baldaro, so you should aim to do most of your running at a steady, moderate pace.

However, we're also going to add a dash of pseudo-speedwork into your endurance stew for flavor. This will put some added spring into your step, give you a brief taste of what it feels like to run a little faster, and hasten your progression to the intermediate level. So, every week, in addition to your steady running, you're going to do two extra things:

> **AEROBIC INTERVALS (AI)** In these, you push the pace a bit—until you breathe just a little harder than usual—followed by slow jogging until you feel rested enough to resume your regular speed, and you always stay well short of going anaerobic (simply stated, that means squinty-eyed and gasping for breath). Treat these runs like play. When you do them, try to

RACING

>>BEGINNER'S 10-K SCHEDULE

WEEK	MON	TUE	WED	THU	FRI	SAT	SUN	TOTAL
1	REST	2 miles, 4 x 1 min AI, 2 miles	3 miles or rest	4 miles + 3 GP	REST	5 miles	Rest	16–20 miles
2	REST	2 miles	3 miles or rest	4 miles + 3 GP	REST	5.5 miles	3.5 miles	18–21 miles
3	REST	2 miles, 4 x 90 secs AI, 2 miles	3 miles or rest	4.5 miles + 3 GP	REST	6 miles	4 miles	18.5–22 miles
4	REST	2 miles, 6 x 90 secs AI, 2 miles	3 miles or rest	4.5 miles + 6 GP	REST	6.5 miles	4.5 miles	20–24 miles
5	REST	2 miles, 4 x 2 mins AI, 2 miles	3 miles or rest	5 miles + 6 GP	REST	7 miles	5 miles	21.5–26 miles
TAPER	REST	2 miles, 3 mins, 2 mins, 1 min AI, 2 miles	2 miles	2 miles + 2 GP	2 miles + 2 GP	REST	10-K Race	

re-create that feeling you had as a child when you ran to the park and couldn't wait to get there.

>**GENTLE PICKUPS (GP)** With pickups, you gradually increase your pace over 100 meters to about 90 percent of all-out, hold it there for 10 to 20 meters, and then gradually decelerate. Walk to full recovery before you start the next one. Nothing big, nothing really stressful—just enough to let your body go. (After a few AI/GP weeks, your normal pace should begin to feel more comfortable, and you'll get race fit more quickly this way.)

>**RACE-DAY RULES** Have something to drink, plus an energy bar or bagel, two hours to 90 minutes before the race, and arrive early enough to make your way to the starting line without great stress. Walk around for about 10 minutes before the start; maybe even do a few minutes of slow jogging. Start off at a slower pace than you think you should, and work gradually into a comfortable and controlled pace. Let the race come to you. If there is a water station, stop to drink and relax for 10 seconds.

>>INTERMEDIATE

Here's the two-pronged approach that will move you from recreational runner to the cusp of competitive athlete. First, you'll be adding miles to your endurance-building long run until it makes up 30 percent of your weekly mileage. Second, you'll now be doing a substantial amount of tempo running aimed at elevating your anaerobic threshold, the speed above which blood lactate starts to accumulate in the system. You can avoid this unpleasantness with regular sustained sessions at just below 10-K pace; that is, tempo-run pace. This will significantly improve your endurance and running efficiency in just six weeks. So your training will include tempo work (PI, below), along with a mix of intervals and uphill running, all of which strengthen running muscles, heart, and related aerobic systems.

Oh, one more thing. Running fast requires effort and some discomfort. Even so, be conservative. If you can't maintain the same pace throughout a given session, or if your body really starts to complain, call it a day and think about adjusting your pace next time.

>**PACE INTERVALS (PI)** Run at target 10-K pace to improve your efficiency and stamina, and to give you the feel of your race pace. For 10-minute/mile pace (a 1:02:06 10-K), run 2:30 (for 400 meters [m]), 5:00 (800 m), 7:30 (1200 m). For nine-minute/mile pace (55:53), run 2:15 (400 m), 4:30 (800 m), 6:45 (1200 m). For 8-minute/mile pace (49:40), run 2:00 (400 m), 4:00 (800 m), 6:00 (1200 m). With pace and speed intervals (below), jog half the interval distance to recover.

>**SPEED INTERVALS (SI)** Run these at 30 seconds per mile faster than race pace.

For 10-minute/mile pace: Run 2:22 (for 400 m), 4:44 (800 m), 7:06 (1200 m).

For nine-minute/mile pace: Run 2:08 (400 m), 4:16 (800 m), 6:24 (1200 m).

For eight-minute/mile pace: Run 1:53 (400 m), 3:45 (800 m), 5:38 (1200 m).

10-10 Run 10-minute tempo repetitions at 30 seconds per mile slower than 10-K goal pace, with three- to five-minute slow jogs after each.

>TOTAL UPHILL TIME (TUT) Run repetitions up the same hill, or work the uphill sections of a road or off-road course.

>STRIDES (S) Over 100 m, gradually accelerate to about 90 percent of all-out, hold it for five seconds, then smoothly decelerate. Walk to full recovery.

>RACE-DAY RULES "Many intermediate runners run too fast in the first half of the race," says running coach Bud Baldaro. "That's just about as close as you can get to a guaranteed way of running a mediocre time. Even pace is best, which means the first half of the race should feel really easy." Divide the race into three two-mile sections: in-control pace for the first two, push a bit the middle two, then go hard the last two and, finally, sprint when you see the line.

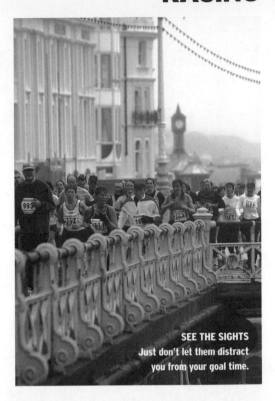

SEE THE SIGHTS
Just don't let them distract you from your goal time.

>>INTERMEDIATE'S 10-K SCHEDULE

WEEK	MON	TUE	WED	THU	FRI	SAT	SUN	TOTAL
1	REST	2 miles, 1-2 x Pl, 2 miles	4 miles	400 meters (m), 800 m, 1200 m, 800 m, 400 m Pl	REST	4 miles + 4 x 100 m S	6-7 miles	24 miles
2	REST	6 miles inc 6 mins TUT	4 miles	1200 m, 2 x 800 m, 4 x 200 m Pl + 4 x 200 m Sl + 4 x 100 m S	REST	4.5 miles + 5 x 100 m S	7-8 miles	26 miles
3	REST	2 miles, 2-3 x Pl, 2 miles	4 miles	800 m, 1200 m, 800 m Pl + 2 x 400 m, 4 x 100 m S	REST	5 miles + 6 x 100 m S	7-8 miles	27.5 miles
4	REST	6-7 miles inc 8 minutes TUT	4 miles	1200 m, 800 m, 2 x 400 m, 2 x 200 m Sl + 4 x 100 m S	REST	5 miles + 6 x 100 m S	8-9 miles	29 miles
5	REST	2 miles, 3-4 x Pl, 2 miles	4 miles	800 m, 4 x 400 m, 4 x 200 m, 800 m Sl, + 4 x 100 m S	REST	6 miles + 6 x 100 m S	8-9 miles	31 miles
TAPER	REST	800 m, 2 x 200 m, 400 m, 2 x 200 m Sl + 6 x 100 m S	4 miles	4 x 200 m Sl + 4 x 100 m S	REST	3 miles easy + 3 x 100 m S	10-K Race	

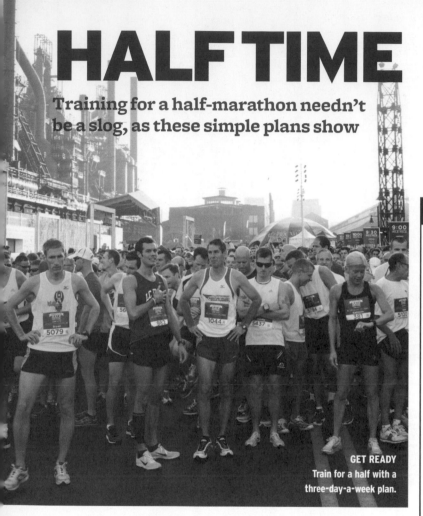

HALF TIME

Training for a half-marathon needn't be a slog, as these simple plans show

GET READY
Train for a half with a three-day-a-week plan.

> **THE HALF-MARATHON** has something for everyone, whether you're a beginner looking to stretch yourself or a marathon runner looking to stay in tune. Training for a half is within reach, as our three-day-a-week beginner's and improver's schedules, devised by coach Nick Anderson, go to show.

The beginner's training schedule lets you run by time and effort, rather than counting miles. It's designed for those new to the half-marathon and builds from 30-minute run/walk sessions to race day over 12 weeks. The improver's program is designed for runners who have run a few half-marathons, but are looking to improve on their best time. "You should certainly be looking at sub 1:50, but I've coached runners who have run under 1:30 for a half on a three-day-weekly schedule," says Anderson. Gauge your effort using your rate of perceived exertion or your maximum heart rate. There's more info on these with the training plans over the following pages.

SIX PRO TIPS

U.S. record holder Ryan Hall, 30, on how to race your best half-marathon
1 IN TRAINING... Don't be afraid of mistakes. You're going to screw up sometimes. If I go out too hard on a tempo run, I think this is good practice for when I go out too fast in a race and have to regroup.
2 SIMULATE RACE CONDITIONS Want to run fast on the road? Do your intervals on the road.
3 KNOW THE PURPOSE OF EACH WORKOUT Make the hard runs hard and the recovery runs easy. Many runners make the mistake of running too hard on their easy days, which is counterproductive.
4 AT THE RACE Inspect the course. Familiarize yourself with landmarks, so you have some mental breaks in addition to mile markers. Look for places to run the tangents if you're going for a PR.
5 LET TERRAIN DICTATE YOUR PACE If you want to average seven-minute miles, it's okay to run 7:10s up the hills and 6:50s down, rather than forcing yourself to stick to sevens the entire way.
6 RUN THE MILE YOU'RE IN I avoid thinking about how far I have to go early in the race, because that can be overwhelming. Late in the race I try to forget about how far I have gone, because that would give me an excuse to give in to fatigue.

IMAGE: NATHAN PERKEL

>>BEGINNER'S HALF-MARATHON SCHEDULE

WEEK	MON	TUE	WED	THU	FRI	SAT or SUN
1	REST	30 mins: 5-min walk/ 5-min run, repeat 3 times Perceived Effort: 5/7	REST	30 mins: 1-min walk/ 1-min easy jog/1-min run, repeat continuously 5/6/7	REST	30 mins: 5-min walk/ 5-min run, repeat 3 times 5/7
2	REST	30 mins: 4-min walk/6-min run, repeat 3 times 5/7	REST	30 mins: 2-min walk/2-min easy jog/2-min run, repeat continuously 5/6/7	REST	30 mins: 4-min walk/6-min run, repeat 3 times 5/7
3	REST	30 mins: 2-min walk/8-min run, repeat 3 times 5/7	REST	30 mins: 2-min walk/2-min easy jog/2-min run, repeat continuously 5/6/7	REST	30 mins: 2-min walk/8-min run, repeat 3 times 5/7
4	REST	30 mins: 2 x 10 mins of continuous easy running. Have a 5-min walk between blocks 7/5/7	REST	45 mins: 3-min walk/3-min jog/3-min threshold run, repeat continuously 5/6-7/8	REST	50 mins: 2-min walk/8-min run, repeat 4 times. Have a 5-min brisk walk warmup & cooldown 5/7
5	REST	20 mins continuous running with 5-min walk warmup and cooldown 5/7/5	REST	Repeat above session	REST	60 mins: 3-min walk/12-min run, repeat 4 times 5/7
6	REST	25 mins continuous running with 5-min walk warmup and cooldown 5/7/5	REST	5-min walk/5-min easy run/ 5-min threshold run, repeat 3 times 5/6-7/8	REST	Repeat above session
7	REST	30 mins easy-pace run with 5-min walk warmup and cooldown 5/7/5	REST	45 mins: 5 x 5-min threshold /2-min walk & 5-min warmup and cooldown 5/8/5	REST	75 mins: 3-min walk/12-min run, repeat 5 times 5/7
8	REST	40 mins easy pace with warmup and cooldown walks 5/7/5	REST	5-min threshold/5-min easy run x 2 with warmup walk/jog and cooldown 5/8/5	REST	Repeat above session
9	REST	45 mins easy pace with warmup and cooldown walks 5/7/5	REST	30 mins: 5-min easy/5-min threshold. Add a 5-min warmup and cooldown jog 5/6-7/8/5	REST	90 mins: 3-min walk/12-min run, repeat 6 times 5/7
10	REST	45 mins easy 6-7	REST	40 mins: 5-min easy/5-min threshold. Add a 5-min warmup and cooldown jog 5/6-7/8/5	REST	100 mins: 18-min easy run/2-min walk, repeat 5 times 5/6-7
11	REST	30 mins: 10 very easy jog/ 10 steady/10 threshold 6/7/8	REST	40 mins easy pace: 2 x 10 mins threshold. Have 5-min jog between efforts 6/8	REST	60 mins: 25 mins easy pace/5 min walk, repeat 2 times 6-7/5
12	REST	30 mins: 5-min easy/5-min threshold, repeat 3 times 6/8	REST	20 mins easy relaxed run 6-7	REST	RACE DAY 15-20 mins easy pace/ walk 5 mins. Drink your fluids while walking. 6-8/5

KEY TO PERCEIVED EFFORT

>5 (out of 10) or 50% maximum heart rate (max HR) A brisk walk.

>6 (out of 10) or 60% max HR Recovery running. This is a very easy running pace that allows you to maintain a conversation with no problems.

>7 (out of 10) or 70% max HR Steady running. A little harder than recovery pace, but you should still be able to hold a conversation.

>8 (out of 10) or 80% max HR Threshold running and target half-marathon pace. You should only be able to say a few words.

AVOID THINKING ABOUT HOW FAR YOU HAVE TO GO EARLY IN THE RACE.

KNOW THE COURSE
Inspect it beforehand to run your best race.

CHART YOUR PROGRESS Proven training rules

The folks at fetcheveryone.com have logged more than 800,000 training sessions and 100,000 race times from runners.

This chart shows how various finishers' training broke down between types of running in percentage terms. Notice how faster finishers do comparatively more warmup and recovery runs, interval, and tempo sessions than other runners. The long run also makes up less of their training schedule.

Finish time (Hr/Mins)

- Warm up & recovery
- Tempo
- Race
- Off road
- Long run
- Intervals/fartleks
- Hill work
- General

This chart shows a breakdown of training-session frequency and mileage for half-marathon finishers in times ranging from 1:15 to 2:30. There are no real secrets to running a fast time—the more you put in, the more you get out.

A 1:15 half-marathon runner, for example, will typically run eight times a week, while a 1:30 finisher trains almost five times a week. But the chart also shows it's possible to run around three times a week and finish in well under two hours.

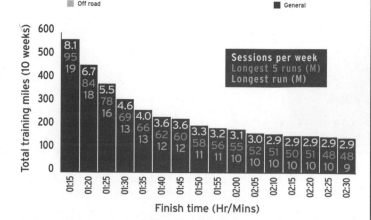

Total training miles (10 weeks)

Sessions per week
Longest 5 runs (M)
Longest run (M)

Finish time	Sessions per week	Longest 5 runs (M)	Longest run (M)
01:15	8.1	95	19
01:20	6.7	84	18
01:25	5.5	78	16
01:30	4.6	69	13
01:35	4.0	66	13
01:40	3.6	62	12
01:45	3.6	60	12
01:50	3.3	58	11
01:55	3.2	56	11
02:00	3.1	55	10
02:05	3.0	52	10
02:10	2.9	51	10
02:15	2.9	50	10
02:20	2.9	51	10
02:25	2.9	48	10
02:30	2.9	48	9

Finish time (Hr/Mins)

IMAGE: NATHAN PERKEL; ILLUSTRATION: FETCHEVERYONE.COM

»IMPROVER'S HALF-MARATHON SCHEDULE

WEEK	MON	TUE	WED	THU	FRI	SAT or SUN
1	REST	10 mins easy/8 mins @ threshold pace, repeat 2 times Perceived Effort: 6-7/8-8.5	REST	10 mins easy, 2 x 5 mins of continuous hills (approx 45 secs up/45 secs down), 10 mins easy 6-7/8-8.5/6-7	REST	60 mins easy 6-7
2	REST	10 mins easy, 10 mins @ threshold pace, repeat 2 times 6-7/8-8.5	REST	10 mins easy, 2 x 7 mins of continuous hills, 10 mins easy 6-7/8-8.5/6-7	REST	70 mins easy 6-7
3	REST	7 mins easy, 7 mins @ threshold pace, repeat 3 times 6-7/8-8.5	REST	10 mins easy, 3 x 5 mins of continuous hills, 10 mins easy 6-7/8-8.5/6-7	REST	75 mins easy 6-7
4	REST	36 mins: 6 x 3 mins, with 3 mins easy in between Reps 1, 3 & 5 @ 6-7; reps 2, 4 & 6 @ 8-8.5	REST	40-min hilly run. Easy but faster up hills 6 if easy, 7-8 on hills	REST	60 mins easy or 10-K race 6-7 or 8-9
5	REST	45 mins relaxed 6-7	REST	10 mins easy, 2 x 10 mins of continuous hills (approx 45 secs up/45 secs down), 10 easy 6-7/8-8.5/6.7	REST	80 mins easy 6-7
6	REST	5 mins easy, 2 x 12 mins @ threshold/HM race pace with 4 mins easy recovery, 5 mins easy 6-7/8-8.5/6-7	REST	10 mins easy, 3 x 7 mins of continuous hills, 10 mins easy 6-7/8-8.5/6.7	REST	80 mins with last 20 mins @ HM race pace 6-7/8
7	REST	45 mins: 15 easy, 15 steady, 15 threshold 6/7/8	REST	40 mins hilly run. Attack the hills, relax rest of run 6-7/8-8.5	REST	60 mins easy 6-7
8	REST	5 mins easy, 3 x 10 mins @ threshold/HM pace, 5 min easy 6-7/8-8.5/6-7	REST	10 mins easy, 3 x 8 mins of continuous hills, 10 mins easy 6-7/8-8.5/6.7	REST	90 mins easy with last 20 mins @ HM race pace 6-7/8
9	REST	10 mins easy, 25 mins @ HM/threshold pace, 10 mins easy 6-7/8-8.5/6-7	REST	10 mins easy, 2 x 6, 4, 2 mins @ HM, 10-K, 5-K pace with 2-min easy between sets, 10 easy 6-7/8-9/6-7	REST	100-110 mins easy 6-7
10	REST	10 mins easy, 5 x 2 mins hard/2 min easy, 10 min easy 6-7/8-9/6-7	REST	45 mins hilly run or 40 mins easy if racing Sunday 6/7 or 8	REST	75 mins easy or 10-K race 6-7 or 9
11	REST	48 mins: 3-min threshold/3-min easy, repeat 8 times 8-8.5/6-7	REST	15 mins easy, 5 x 3 mins @ 10-K pace with 2-min easy recovery between each rep, 15 mins easy 6-7/9/6-7	REST	60 mins easy 6-7
12	REST	30 mins: 5 mins easy/ 5 mins @ threshold, repeat 3 times 6-7/8-8.5	REST	20 mins easy 6	REST	HALF-MARATHON RACE 8

KEY TO PERCEIVED EFFORT

>6 (out of 10) or 60% maximum heart rate (max HR) Recovery running. An easy pace that allows you to maintain a conversation.

>7 (out of 10) or 70% max HR Steady running. A little harder than recovery pace, but you should still be able to hold a conversation.

>8-8.5 (out of 10) or 80-85% max HR Threshold running and target half-marathon pace. It hurts, and you should only be able to speak a few words at a time.

>8.5+ (out of 10) or 85%+ of max HR This is just below your maximum effort and you won't be able to speak. Use for short intervals and speedwork.

10 RULES OF MARATHON TRAINING

When it comes to marathon prep, there isn't one right plan. But these principles will help you figure out what works—for you

> **WHAT'S THE BEST WAY TO TRAIN FOR A MARATHON?** Well, according to a recent report in the *International Journal of Sport Physiology and Performance*, there isn't one. A study of 93 elite marathoners found that there were no universal themes when it came to preparation for the 26.2-miler.

But it's not all bad. While marathon training hasn't been studied extensively, millions of runners have gone the distance. And when you look at the science and shared knowledge of marathon training, these overarching principles emerge.

1 RUN JUST ENOUGH

"Stay healthy" is the most important piece of training advice, and the most often ignored. It does you no good to train hard, and then get sick or injured. Better to be slightly undertrained, but feeling strong and eager, than to be overtrained. The trick, of course, is finding that fine line between the two.

2 BUILD YOUR TRAINING SLOWLY

Increase weekly mileage by just 10 percent every week. Extend long runs by just one mile at a time up to 10 miles, then by two miles at a time if you want. Take recovery weeks as well as recovery days. Here's what eight weeks of training might look like, in terms of miles per week: 20-22-24-20-26-28-30-20.

3 RECOVER, RECOVER, RECOVER

You don't have to train hard seven days a week. You just have to train smart three or four days a week. This was proven in a 1994 study at the University of Northern Iowa, where four-time-a-week runners performed just as well in a marathon as those training six times a week and covering 20 percent more miles.

4 DO YOUR LONG RUNS

This is a no-brainer. The newer you are to marathon running, the more important your long runs. You simply have to become accustomed to being on your feet for three, four, or more hours. There's no magic length. Most experts recommend stopping at two-and-a-half to three hours, but you could try going farther and include walk breaks. All systems work, as long as you get to the starting line healthy and strong.

5 PRACTICE YOUR MARATHON PACE

Makes sense, doesn't it? The key is adding Progressive Marathon-Pace (MP) long runs to your program. For example, try a two-mile warmup, then do six miles at MP + 40 seconds, six more at MP + 20, and your final six at MP.

6 EXTEND YOUR TEMPO-RUN DISTANCE

Tempo runs were born as four-mile efforts, propounded by coach Jack Daniels. Then another coach, Joe Vigil, asked elite runner Deena Kastor to hold the tempo pace longer—eventually up to 12 miles. He got another of his protégés, Meb Keflezighi, to 15. The result? Two Olympic Marathon medals. Gradually extend your tempo runs, slowing by a few seconds per mile from your four-mile pace. "The longer the tempo run workout you can sustain, the greater the dividends down the road," says Vigil.

IMAGE: GETTY

TRAIN TO GAIN
The right preparation can help make those 26.2 miles fly by.

7 EAT YOUR CARBS...

To stay healthy and recover well, you need to fuel your body efficiently. First, consume carbs—gel, sports drink, and so on—during long, hard workouts to keep strong. Second, have a good helping of carbs as soon as possible after workouts. This will replenish the glycogen (energy supply) in your depleted leg muscles. Add some protein for muscle repair.

8 ...AND PAY ATTENTION TO IRON

None of the marathon runners in the *International Journal of Sport Physiology and Performance* study identified themselves as "vegetarians." Running increases iron loss through sweating and pounding. You don't have to be a meat-eater to run a strong marathon, but you do have to consume enough iron. Consuming iron-rich foods with vitamin C, which increases the body's iron absorption, will help.

9 SIDESTEP INJURIES

If he were 22 years old again, two-time Olympic marathon runner Peter Pfitzinger, who competed in the 1984 and 1988 Games and is the author of *Advanced Marathoning*, says he'd rest and/or cross-train for several days a week at the first hint of a problem. And that he'd include core training in his regimen. "I'm convinced that core stability helps runners maintain good running form and pace late in a race," says Pfitzinger.

10 TAPER FOR TWO TO THREE WEEKS

Many runners hate to taper. We are cursed with a sort of sublime obsessiveness—a big help when you're increasing your efforts, but an albatross when you're supposed to be cutting back. A new study from Ball State University, Indiana, showed a particular gain in Type IIa muscle-fiber strength—the so-called fast, aerobic muscles that can adapt to improve your performance—after a three-week taper.

KEY WORKOUTS FOR YOUR BEST 26.2

MILE REPEATS

When it comes to marathon training, veteran 26.2-milers swear by this modified form of tempo training. You should run each mile repeat about 20 seconds faster than your predicted marathon goal pace, with a 400-meter recovery walk or jog. You'll get the best results if you can build up to 10- to 13-mile repeats.

YASSO 800S

The goal, after several months of working up to it, is to run 10 x 800 meters in the same minutes:seconds as your goal time (in hours:minutes). If you want to run a 3:40 marathon, for example, you run your Yasso 800s in 3 minutes, 40 seconds. This workout isn't based on physiology; it's a good hard workout.

HERE'S THE PLAN

Bart Yasso's race-tested intermediate marathon-training program

WEEK	MON	TUE	WED	THU	FRI	SAT	SUN	TOTAL
	REST	Easy	Hard Work: Hills, Speed	REST	Easy or MP	Easy	Long, Slow Distance (LSD)	MILES
1	REST	Easy 4 miles	6 miles hills	REST	Easy 4 miles	Easy 4 miles	7 miles LSD	25
2	REST	Easy 4 miles	6 miles hills	REST	Easy 5 miles	Easy 5 miles	9 miles LSD	29
3	REST	Easy 3 miles	6 miles hills	REST	Easy 5 miles	Easy 5 miles	12 miles LSD	31
4	REST	Easy 4 miles	6 miles hills	REST	Easy 4 miles	Easy 4 miles	10 miles LSD	28
5	REST	Easy 4 miles	7 miles hills	REST	Easy 4 miles	Easy 4 miles	13 miles LSD	32
6	REST	Easy 7 miles	8 miles hills	REST	Easy 6 miles	Easy 6 miles	2-mile warmup, 5-K race, 1-mile cooldown TOTAL: 6 miles	33
7	REST	Easy 4 miles	7 miles hills	REST	Easy 5 miles	Easy 5 miles	16 miles LSD	37
8	REST	Easy 5 miles	HILL REPEATS: TOTAL: 8 miles	REST	Easy 4 miles	Easy 4 miles	14 miles LSD	35
9	REST	Easy 3 miles	MILE REPEATS 2-mile warmup, 3 x 1 mile @ 10-K pace, w/ 400-meter recovery, 2-mile cooldown TOTAL: 8 miles	REST	1-mile warmup, 7 miles @ MP, 1-mile cooldown TOTAL: 9 miles	Easy 3 miles	18 miles LSD	41

10	REST	Easy 4 miles	YASSO 800s 2-mile warmup, 6 x 800 meters w/ 400-meter recovery, 2-mile cooldown TOTAL: 9 miles	REST	1-mile warmup, 8 miles @ MP, 1-mile cooldown TOTAL: 10 miles	Easy 4 miles	20 miles LSD	47
11	REST	Easy 4 miles	Easy 7 miles	REST	1-mile warmup, 8 miles @ MP, 1-mile cooldown TOTAL: 10 miles	Easy 4 miles	20 miles LSD	45
12	REST	Easy 7 miles	MILE REPEATS 2-mile warmup, 4 x 1 mile @ 10-K pace, w/ 800-meter recovery, 2-mile cooldown TOTAL: 10 miles	REST	Easy 7 miles	Easy 8 miles	15 miles LSD	47
13	REST	Easy 6 miles	YASSO 800s 2-mile warmup, 8 x 800 w/ 400-meter recovery, 2-mile cooldown TOTAL: 10 miles	REST	Easy 6 miles	Easy 6 miles	22 miles LSD	50
14	REST	Easy 8 miles	MILE REPEATS 2-mile warmup, 3 x 1 mile @ 10-K pace w/ 400-meter recovery, 2-mile cooldown TOTAL: 8 miles	REST	Easy 7 miles	Easy 7 miles	15 miles LSD	45
15	REST	Easy 5 miles	Easy 4 miles	REST	Easy 6 miles	Easy 5 miles	12 miles LSD	32
16	REST	Easy 5 miles	REST	Easy 5 miles	REST	Very easy 3 miles	Race day	13

KEY

REST DAYS Ideally, don't exercise. At most, cross-train with a no-impact activity like stretching, yoga, or swimming.
EASY DAYS Run at a comfortable pace or cross-train with a sustained aerobic effort.
HILLS Run the mileage for the day on the hilliest route you can plot. These sessions build strength in the first seven weeks.

HILL REPEATS On week eight, find a hill that will take you at least two minutes to climb, and mark off a short repeat, halfway from the bottom, and a long repeat to the top. After a two-mile warmup, run to the short mark three or four times, jogging back down to recover. Then run to the top three or four times, jogging back down to the short mark, then sprinting to the

bottom. Finish with three or four sprints up to the short mark. Cool down with two miles of easy running.
SPEEDWORK (MILE REPEATS AND YASSO 800S) Warm up/cool down with two easy miles. For mile repeats, run a mile at your 10-K pace, jog a lap for recovery, and repeat three times. For the 800s, run 800 meters at a time equivalent

to your marathon time. For example, if you're aiming for a 4:10 marathon, run each 800 in four minutes and 10 seconds. Jog 400 meters in between.
LSD Long, slow distance runs build endurance. These should be done at an easy pace, one to two minutes slower than your marathon goal pace.
MP Marathon goal pace—the speed you hope to hit in the race.

GETTING YOU TO 26.2

Ten marathon runners offer tips for being at your best on race day

1 TAKE NOTE

"For me the biggest thing in the early stages of marathon training was fear of the unknown," says Lina Martino. "I'd only just taken up running and had no idea whether I was capable of running 26.2 miles, and there were times I seriously doubted I could. Keeping a detailed training log so that I had a record of how I was progressing really helped. Seeing even the smallest progress in black and white really boosted my confidence. It also helped me keep things in perspective when I'd run an 18-miler slower than I'd hoped."

2 PREEMPT TO PREVENT

Pilates instructor Tim Hawes found that preempting injuries helped him in his marathon battle. "I've always suffered from tight hamstrings and decided to try a technique called myofascial release," he says. "Standing, I'd put as much weight as was bearable on a tennis ball, then roll it around under the sole of my foot, getting into sore spots. Just two minutes a day on each foot had an amazing effect—I could stretch much better immediately afterward and over the course of several days noticed how much deeper my stretch was."

3 CLOCK-WATCHING

"Think of a long run in terms of X hours, not in terms of miles," says Susan Kennedy. "Just set off, and instead of worrying about how fast you're going, enjoy the run, knowing you can't make time pass more quickly. It takes all the anxiety and tedium out of it. The miles fly by with you hardly noticing. Time on your feet counts for twice as much as speed when you're tackling your first marathon—just getting used to the sensation of running for that amount of time is a big hurdle, and once you're mentally prepped for that, it's all downhill."

4 GET TOUGHER

Sometimes you need to prove to yourself that you're prepared to handle the worst that Mother Nature can throw at you before you're psychologically ready to tackle the arduous training, says Sarah Chapman. "I'd watch the weather forecast and make a point of scheduling training for unpleasant weather to help develop the determination and robustness required to cross the finish line," she says. "The only weather conditions that present a genuine excuse for skipping training are ice and hail storms combined with high winds. Everything else is simply a test of resolve."

5 MAKE A CONTRACT

For a spring marathon the early stages are in deepest winter, which for Andy Gwyther meant dark, cold, early-morning sessions. "Getting into a routine of consistency is key early on. I would write down what I was going to do before going to bed the night before as a way of making it non-negotiable in my mind when the alarm went off at 5:45 a.m.," he says. "It's easy to slack off when it gets tough, so I repeat to myself that if I can't push on now, I won't be able to in the actual race either. I imagine the last five to 10 minutes is the end of the race to keep me strong."

6 TAKE BREAKS

When it came to increasing the length of long runs, Mary Wilkinson struggled toward the end and was exhausted afterward. "It's not easy to slow down when you're a naturally fast runner," she says. "I overcame this by starting at my normal long-run pace, then walking for a minute after every 20 minutes I ran. Even if I felt great after 20 minutes, I made myself stop, which meant I was able to cope with much longer runs. As my training progressed, I lengthened the duration of the steady sections and was eventually able to do the whole long run at my usual pace. Knowing there's a break approaching is far easier mentally."

7 PAY THE PROS

"One thing that really helped me in my first marathon was finding a chiropractor I trusted," says Garry Cochrane. "From day one I was plagued with a groin strain, but regular chiropractor sessions really helped me cope with the problem, giving me confidence. The advice meant I could continue to train, as I was reassured that nothing was going to snap or fall off and that it wouldn't get any worse. On race day there was no sign or feeling of the injury at all."

8 BE FLEXIBLE

Remember that any marathon training schedule is not cast in stone—it's just a route map, advises marathon veteran Peter Russell. "It's to get you from where you are now to where you want to be, and nothing more," he says. "There are plenty of 'alternative routes' on the way. If you don't achieve one goal, or a week's planned runs, then take a diversion—we all have bad days/weeks and get lost on the way. It isn't the end of the world. Just adjust the schedule and relax. It's a strategy that's helped me tackle nine marathons and enjoy every one."

9 DISTRACTION TACTICS

"For me, the mental part is harder than the physical part—and the physical part is hard enough," says Johnny Christmas. "I found running alone really difficult, and sometimes my heart sank knowing I would have to get out on a miserable day and do 18 miles plodding through mud on my own. Having an iPod was great—listening to podcasts or music helped pass the time."

10 FIGHT THE FREEZE

The obvious problem of starting any training schedule in midwinter isn't one you should take lightly, says Grant Wooler. "In the winter my hands get agonizingly cold—then I had a brainstorm that I could combine my need for hydration on longer runs with keeping my hands warm. I'd fill my water bottle up with almost boiling water from the kettle, which would keep my hands warm for about eight miles, by which time my body was generating enough of its own heat. And by that time you need some hydration, when it is cool enough to drink."

ILLUSTRATION: DANNY ALLISON

RUN A PERFECT RACE

The alarm clock rings—now what? Here's how to navigate any course correctly

> **TO RACE WELL, YOU NEED TO TRAIN WELL**—that much is obvious. But there are also race-day logistics to master. Even if training has gone like a dream, you can still blow everything by tearing around on race morning in a manic panic in search of safety pins, finding yourself at the starting line with a jumble of jingling keys, or getting held up midrace trying to pass an iPod-wearing runner. So, to make sure your hard training doesn't go to waste, we've compiled all the advice you need to successfully navigate race day. Our tips start before the start, finish after the finish, and—if employed properly—will guarantee a glitch-free race (and maybe even a PR).

ILLUSTRATIONS: ERIK JOHNSON

››BEFORE THE GUN

Your prerace goal should be to arrive at the starting line relaxed and ready to run. Here's how to do it.

LAY IT OUT

"The night before your race, lay out everything you'll need for the day on an extra bed or the floor," says Greg McMillan, running coach and director of McMillan Running. With the race start still half a day

away, you can think clearly about all the things you want with you on the morning itself.

TRAVEL LIGHT

You could save yourself the postrace hassle of retrieving your belongings by not checking anything into the baggage hold area. Wear an old sweatshirt and jogging pants over your racing outfit that you can toss at the start (most races donate the clothes). "Only 50 out of 37,000 runners might not get back what they left at the start," says Dave Bedford, race director of the London Marathon. If you need to check your bag in, don't put anything in your sack that you can't live without (such as your keys; see "Secure Your Key," below).

SHOW YOUR NUMBER

Even though most races time with chips, you still have to wear a number. "Bib numbers show race officials that you are a registered runner," says Bedford. "They should be visible at all times." Pin your bib on the front of your racing outfit with four safety pins to keep it from flapping around.

SECURE YOUR KEY

Find somewhere to stash your car key (note: singular), but not where someone might find it, like in the gas cap or on top of a tire. If the key is not too bulky, slide it into a zip-up pocket or lace it into your shoe. You could also hand your keys to a spectator friend—as long as he has a nicer car than yours.

STASH SOME CASH

If you have money with you for an emergency, you won't need it. If you don't, you will. So pin a $20 bill—inside a freezer bag to prevent it from getting soggy—inside your vest, or put it in the pocket of your shorts, just in case.

BAG YOURSELF

They're not stylish, but plastic trash bags do keep you warm and dry if it's cold and raining. "Cut a hole for just your head, and tuck your arms inside," recommends Bedford.

WARM UP WISELY

If possible, warm up by running the first mile or so of the racecourse to get the lay of the land. If you can't do that, warm up on a nearby road or sidewalk, not in a grassy field—early morning dew can soak through your shoes and socks.

RACING

ILLUSTRATIONS: JASON LEE, ERIK JOHNSON

GO AS A RUNNER

If you must dress up in a costume, "make sure it doesn't interfere with other runners," says Chris Sumner, race director of the Robin Hood Festival of Running. "Always show consideration toward others. For your own safety, make sure you can run in the outfit if it's heavy, and practice beforehand."

LINE UP ON TIME

Don't get there first, because the extra wait will only make you anxious. Instead, watch the clock and keep an eye on runners as they fill in behind the start. Then join in. Many races have signs showing you where to stand according to your predicted pace. What if your race doesn't have markers? If you're hoping to run a four-hour (or longer) marathon, don't line up within 100 yards of a Kenyan.

>>AND YOU'RE OFF!

Once the race starts, there's more to think about than just putting one foot in front of the other.

WAIT!

"Don't start your watch at the gun," recommends McMillan. It's hard to resist when you're keen to get going, but starting your watch immediately after the starting gun will yield a depressing finishing time, because it might take several minutes to cross the starting line. Turn your watch face inside your wrist to avoid an accidental bump that might activate the stopwatch, then hit the start button when you reach the starting line. This will synchronize your chip time and your watch time, so you can accurately calculate your pace.

LOOK FOR ROOM

As you ramp up to race pace, try to achieve "daylight" between you and other runners, which is basically two full stride lengths.

BE PATIENT

Don't bob and weave through the starting pack. You'll waste energy without getting very far. Instead, jog or walk with your arms slightly out to help you keep your balance. And be sure not to follow the guy with the headband who has jumped onto the curb and is sprinting ahead. The race gods will, without question, make him trip.

DRINK SECOND

The first water stop in larger races often resembles a crowded train station at rush hour. As long as you're not thirsty, skip it. "If you don't need the water, then don't get involved for the sake of it," says Sumner. "Try to avoid the crush and focus on getting to the next water station." If you need to, start with a water bottle, drink along the way, and discard it when you're done. You can refuel at later drink stations once the field has thinned out.

PASS WITH CAUTION

Runners listening to MP3 players are in a world of their own and can't hear you behind them, so they probably don't know that you're approaching. "If you do come across someone wearing headphones," advises Sumner, "slow down slightly, concentrate on the whole picture around you, and take a wide berth while making sure not to interfere with anyone else."

RACE-READY CHECKLIST What to pack on the big day

1 Baseball cap and/or sunglasses: Either will be helpful if you'll be running into the sun (research this beforehand) or rain.

2 Vest: At the very least you'll feel faster.

3 Bib number: Take four safety pins and secure one to each corner—any fewer will cause flopping.

4 Digital stopwatch: So you can be your own clock.

5 Emergency cash: A $20 bill pinned to your vest or in a pocket of your shorts.

6 Cotton gloves: Cheap, they'll keep your hands warm, and they double as a hankie for midrace nose or face wiping.

7 Throwaway shirt and/or trash bag: The shirt will keep you warm before the start; the bag will keep you warm and dry.

8 Running shorts: Your favorite, comfiest, speediest pair. Now is not the time to try anything brand new.

9 Socks: Ankle-high or lower, no cotton (to reduce blister risk).

10 Running shoes: See number 8.

11 Timing chip: Fasten to your shoe with the secure tie (no lacing required).

12 Car key: Lace into the shoe that doesn't have the timing chip.

13 Sunscreen: Be smart—you might be out there a while.

14 Vaseline or some other sports lubricant: Apply the lubricant to your inner thighs, armpits, and, ahem, other spots where you're likely to chafe.

15 Roll of toilet paper: In case the porta potties come up empty.

TURN TACTICS How to be ahead of the curve on race day

DON'T CUT CORNERS

"The quickest way to take a corner is actually to slow down going into it," says Sumner. "The most important thing is not to cut corners. You might think you're saving time by cutting on the inside, but if you jump the curb or mount a grassy stretch at speed, you're asking for an accident. Slow down and take a slightly wider curve going into the corner, then move to the inside and accelerate away."

SAVE SOME STRIDES

If you run along the outside of a curve, you will run more distance than if you take the tangent, which is a straight line between the beginning and end of the curve. "Tangents are the shortest distance between two points—and that's how the course was measured," says McMillan. "So running the tangents doesn't make the course shorter. But it doesn't make it longer."

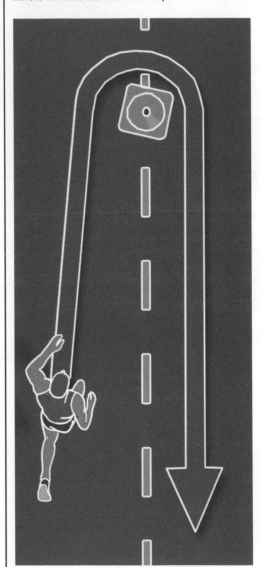

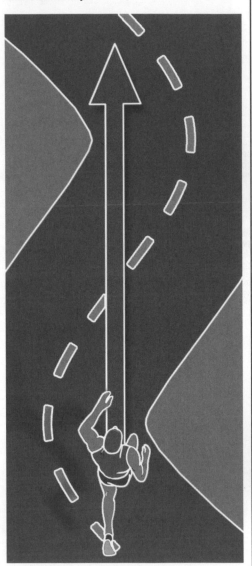

ILLUSTRATIONS: JASON LEE, ERIK JOHNSON

>>HAPPY ENDINGS

As you cross the finish line, you're not quite done yet: The finishing funnel stretches ahead.

TAKE THE WRAP

Worn like a cape, mylar blankets keep the heat in. And if you're offered a sticker or piece of tape with the cape, use it to secure the blanket at the neck so that you can keep your hands free. Note: It doesn't matter which side of the blanket is in and which is out. It traps your body heat either way.

DITCH THE CHIP

If you've used one of those secure plastic ties to attach your chip to your shoe, it takes the volunteers about two seconds to get it off. "Another efficient way is to lace the chip into the shoe just below the knot so all you have to do is untie your shoe to get it off," says Mike Burns, president of ChampionChip. "If the chip is laced further down, below the eyelets and along the tongue, you'll have to unlace the shoe to remove it."

DRINK UP

Even though you are no longer running, you need fluids to rehydrate and recover. Take some and keep moving. Don't stop now, or you risk being knocked around by fellow disoriented competitors.

FIND YOUR FAMILY

Have a prearranged spot to meet up with your family and friends after the race. Anything solid and immovable is best, such as a tree or the front steps of a building. Don't suggest something like the middle of a field, which could be jam-packed with runners come race day. Next, make sure you spot your group before they see you. Now start limping (cue the sympathy violins). But do so with a huge smile on your face.

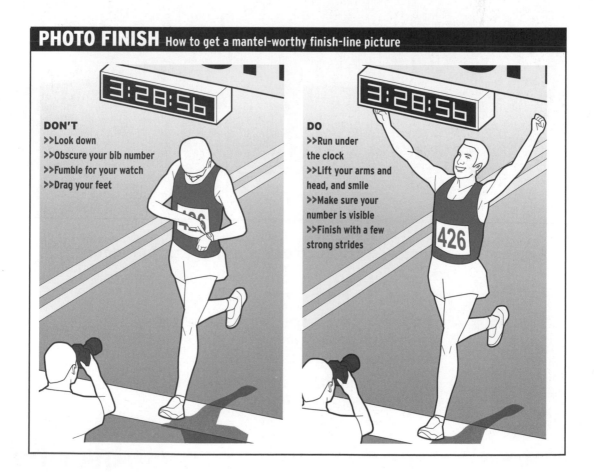

PHOTO FINISH How to get a mantel-worthy finish-line picture

3:28:56

DON'T
>>Look down
>>Obscure your bib number
>>Fumble for your watch
>>Drag your feet

DO
>>Run under the clock
>>Lift your arms and head, and smile
>>Make sure your number is visible
>>Finish with a few strong strides

426

> SUBSCRIBE TO

RUNNER'S WORLD®

> Monthly motivation delivered right to your door!

> Page after page of world-class advice from top coaches, fitness experts, and pro runners

> Timeless tips for race-day success, injury prevention, performance-boosting superfoods, and the best training techniques on Earth

> Can't-miss annual shoe guide, nutrition issue, half-marathon special, and more!

www.runnersworld.com/subscribe